Department of the Environment

The Control of Noise at Surface Mineral Workings

Report prepared by:
WS Atkins Engineering Sciences Ltd

On behalf of:
Department of the Environment

LONDON: HMSO

D
622.3
WSA

STEERING COMMITTEE

We wish to thank the following experts who gave us their time and invaluable advice during the project.

Mr J Adams	British Coal Opencast Executive
Mr J Tomlinson	British Coal Opencast Executive
Mr J Wooliscroft	British Coal Opencast Executive
Dr W Uttley	Building Research Establishment
Mr W Heatherington	Derwentside District Council
Mr J Chatten	Staffordshire County Council
Mr J Gregory	ARC Limited
Mr J Lodge	Northumberland County Council
Mr W Walton	Allerdale District Council
Mr R Johnson	Health and Safety Executive

ACKNOWLEDGMENTS

Acknowledgments are due to Peter Moore, who undertook the field measurements and survey work and who drafted much of the report. Also to Ron Hawkes who advised on, and analysed, the Ffos Las social survey work and revised the report; Kate Gentles who undertook the programming of the noise prediction methods; Alan Rew, Eric Hirsch and David Morgan who undertook most of the social survey field work; Stuart Dryden, who implemented the noise monitoring system; and Geoff Leventhall, the original project manager. Also to the technicians and secretarial staff of WS Atkins Engineering Sciences, without whom the project could not have been completed. Finally, our thanks to Robin Mabey, Peter Bedson and Alastair Bishop of the Department of the Environment for their patient help and guidance through the project.

TABLE OF CONTENTS

LIST OF TABLES

LIST OF FIGURES

LIST OF APPENDICES

1.0 INTRODUCTION

In December 1985, the Department of the Environment announced its intention to commission a research project on the control of noise from surface mineral workings. The objectives of the research were:-

(i)   To determine the most effective methods and practices for reducing noise arising from the extraction of minerals at the surface;

(ii)   To determine the most appropriate means of assessing noise nuisance from intermittent and tonal sources;

(iii)   To investigate the reliability and use of noise monitoring and measurement procedures currently in use, and to establish cost-effective sampling procedures for the measurement of noise from surface mineral workings;

(iv)   To investigate the use and availability of noise reduction techniques;

(v)   To assess and, if necessary, improve the application of predictive noise models to the surface extraction of minerals; and

(vi)   To assess the importance of noise as a factor affecting the public's attitude to surface mineral workings.

The overall purpose of this research was to advise the Department on noise control and to provide the basis for possible future Departmental guidance on the control of noise at surface mineral sites.

The first part of the research consisted of a study of existing practices in the prediction, monitoring, and abatement of noise at mineral sites. The second part of the research consisted of a set of noise monitoring and prediction studies at four mineral sites. Two of these sites were open cast coal mines, one was a sand and gravel pit, and the other was a limestone quarry. Two social surveys were also carried out to assess the impact of noise from mineral sites on the local community.

This report sets out the main findings and recommendations arising from this research.

2.0   SUMMARY OF FINDINGS

It is essential to set out conditions for the control of noise at the planning stage if acceptable levels of noise are to be subsequently achieved at a mineral working site. However, the approaches of Mineral Planning Authorities (MPAs) and mineral operators to noise issues at the planning stage varies widely. There is no specific guidance currently available on the subject. Authorities are therefore forced to use a mixture of their own past experiences, the British Standard 4142 assessment method (which is not appropriate to mineral sites), and the case histories of previous planning applications. There is a need for an assessment procedure which will apply countrywide, and which would be accepted both by local authorities and the site operators.

This research suggests, however, that some current noise control practices can be successful, for the extent of complaints about noise is less than might be expected and the level of complaints is also less significant than for some other environmental effects of mineral workings. Baffle mounds, the screening of fixed plant, site layout and restrictions on the hours of working can play a major part in reducing unacceptable noise emissions. Good relations between the site operator and the local community can also increase the acceptability of noise from the site. The major cause of annoyance at mineral sites was often vehicle reversing alarms, though the use of new directional alarms might reduce the level of annoyance. There is also often concern at the effects of off-site traffic movements.

Although there are no standard guidelines, current practice seems to be moving towards the setting of 65 dB L_{Aeq} (12 hour) noise limits at the site boundary as a planning condition. This practice seems to be generally successful in ensuring acceptable noise levels for local people.

In assessing the acceptability of a minerals development proposal at the planning stage, it is necessary to have a model for predicting the level of noise that is likely to arise. Although the BS5228 noise prediction model was not specifically designed for mineral sites, it does provide accurate predictions when some adjustments are made for haul roads and for soft ground absorption.

There have also been advances in noise monitoring techniques. Noise should be measured in terms of L_{Aeq} using Type 1 (precision) grade equipment as defined by BS5969. Monitoring need only take place for one hour time periods; results from longer monitoring time periods generally do not significantly differ from those obtained from one hour monitoring periods. The equipment should be manned so that extraneous noise (eg. passing aircraft) can be cut out by operating the "pause" button.

Monitoring can be carried out at either noise-sensitive properties near to the site or at the boundary of the site. Although the people who are affected by the noise will be found in the noise-sensitive properties, monitoring noise levels there may be made more difficult by problems of access; such locations are also more affected by extraneous noise.

New noise prediction and monitoring techniques make it possible for more precise noise limit planning conditions to be set than is the current practice. Limits should be initially set at the facades of noise sensitive properties near to the proposed mineral site. These should be in the region of 55-60 dB L_{Aeq} (one hour) during daytime and 40-45 dB at night as these are the levels of noise which are generally acceptable without causing nuisance. The prediction model should then be used to work back and calculate the level of noise at the site boundary which would be equivalent to these noise levels at the facades of the properties. These noise levels at the site boundary should then be stipulated in planning conditions and monitored in the prescribed manner.

3.0 REVIEW OF CURRENT PRACTICES

3.1 Introduction

The starting point of this research, presented in this chapter, was to obtain an appreciation of the extent of problems associated with noise from surface mineral workings; the methods being used to deal with problems; and to evaluate the success of these methods.

In the best current practice, noise control starts at the site planning stage with an assessment of the noise likely to be emitted from the site. This assessment is compared with a criterion related to noise-sensitive buildings and other land uses. Where the noise might be excessive, abatement measures are applied to the proposals. Noise control conditions, usually in the form of limits on noise levels and hours of working, are then written into planning conditions. Noise monitoring during the lifetime of the site provides the checks for compliance with these conditions.

Where best current practice is used, the problem of noise from surface mineral workings appears to be well under control: but owing to a lack of standard procedures, there is a wide variation in practice, leading to unsatisfactory results in some circumstances - either providing inadequate protection to the local community, or being unduly restrictive to operators.

3.2 Methodology

Following a literature review, described in Appendix A, questionnaires were sent to mineral planning authorities and environmental health departments. The questionnaires were supplemented by visits to those authorities and major site operators which were able to provide additional assistance, and to review in detail their current approach to the question.

3.3 Noise prediction

3.3.1 Purpose of prediction

The likely impact of surface mineral workings is generally held to
depend predominantly on (a) the amount of noise emitted from the
site; (b) the proximity of noise-sensitive buildings (or other
noise-sensitive land uses); (c) ambient noise levels; and (d) the
times of occurrence and duration of the intruding noise.

Some or all of these factors may be unknown when a planning
application is received and, certainly in the past, have proved to be
difficult to ascertain in advance of the workings commencing.

The purpose of noise prediction is to determine the amount of noise
which will be emitted from the site and the amount of noise which
will be received at sensitive locations.

It is used to design and determine the acceptability of the proposed
methods of working, the plant to be used and the effectiveness of
noise control measures.

At its most basic level, an assessment may be based solely on
previous subjective experience of sites which are thought to be
similar to that proposed. In cases where the proposal is of a
small-scale nature, or where there are no properties affected, this
approach might be acceptable.

However, a subjective approach could be indicative of a superficial
treatment of the potential problems, carrying a significant risk that
noise limits may be set without verification that they are
technically and economically feasible, which would render them
unenforceable.

3.3.2 Prediction techniques

Consequently, noise assessments are usually made using a so-called prediction method, most commonly that defined in BS5228:1984 "Noise Control on Contruction and Open Sites", which is examined in greater detail in Section 4.1.

This prediction document provides information on the noise produced by a wide range of construction plant and operations, with a set of mathematical charts and formulae to allow the user to calculate the noise level arising at any distance from the site. To use the method, it is necessary to know what plant will be employed, the amount of time it will be in use, the distance of the reception point from the plant and whether there is any screening.

On most sites, many different items of plant are in use at any one time, although the actual items in use and their working position vary from day to day. The total noise is usually calculated on a daily basis by adding together the contributions of noise from each item of plant, to arrive at the equivalent continuous sound level, L_{Aeq}, an average noise level over the calculation period. To obtain the L_{Aeq}, the measuring instrument is given a sensitivity to sounds of different pitch which is similar to the human ear. This is called the 'A-weighting'. The instrument then averages the noise energy arriving at the reception point. This unit of measurement is considered to give a reasonable indication of the subjective effect of the noise.

A primary difficulty with noise prediction is the need to be able to determine the type and quantity of plant at an early stage if reliable results are to be achieved: however it must be pointed out that if this information is not known, then no other method can yield a more accurate assessment of noise impact.

In practice, the quality of noise prediction work also varies considerably with the availability and experience of the staff both in noise predictions and in minerals operations. For this reason, mineral planning authorities often draw on the experience of their environmental health departments for calculation and measurement exercises. The quality of prediction work is also dependent on the level of detail which is forthcoming, which may depend on the amount of trust between the planning authority and the applicant. Frequently, applicants are fearful of revealing anything which may jeopardise their application, whilst planners may mistrust the sincerity of the promises and claims made by applicants.

3.3.3 Current application of prediction techniques

The following case studies help to illustrate the variety of circumstances which occur.

A certain county council in the south-east is the planning authority for about 40 sand and gravel workings. In this county's assessments, the noise from a proposed site is initially predicted through a simple calculation of sound pressure levels at noise sensitive properties, based on the typical sound power levels given in BS5228 for the equipment that is to be used, together with a site plan for measuring distances. The analysis is carried out by the County Surveyor's Department, which makes recommendations to the County Planning Officer.

If the initial analysis indicates a potential noise problem, the analysis may be repeated. The second analysis uses sound power level data for the specific make and model of machinery whose use is proposed, and detailed surveys of the existing background levels are carried out. Consideration is given to noise suppression of machinery and the most effective positioning of baffle mounds. However, no allowance is apparently made in the calculations for the duration of each noise source relative to the total operating time of the site, so in effect it is assumed that all the noise sources are operating all of the time that the site is working. As the applications mostly relate to sand and gravel quarries, this may not be an unreasonable planning assumption.

If a refused application is taken to appeal, this County prepares its Proof of Evidence based mainly on the calculations made for the initial application. Further evidence may be collected, if available, of noise levels from operating sites similar in character to the proposed site. The County will also analyse any alternative methods of working suggested by the applicant.

This is a good level of detail, but some county councils go further. Rather than making their predictions effectively in terms of a maximum dB(A) level, they estimate L_{Aeq} average level accordance with BS5228, by taking into account the lengths of time for which the various items of machinery are operating.

In cases where a planning application is received for an extension to existing workings, some authorities make predictions of noise based on levels from the existing site but adjusted to take account of the distances of the proposed extension from noise-sensitive properties. Examples of this practice have been found in the Midlands in connection with a sand and gravel extraction site (for which the noise calculations were made by a consultant), and in South Wales relating to the extension of existing limestone quarries.

Many County Councils seldom have to tackle the question of predicting noise levels from surface mineral workings, although this does not relieve them of responsibility when the question arises. One such County has only one sand and gravel site in its jurisdiction for which noise has been a prime consideration. When considering the application, the County obtained data specific to the machinery that would be used and made calculations in accordance with the principles of BS5228.

Where an applicant prepares his own predictions, the MPA's will take note of them, particularly when the applicant is a well-established operator. Large operators are involved in the preparation of many applications and can justify the employment of staff to deal primarily with noise. Smaller companies tend to make use of consultants since they seldom need to make noise calculations; alternatively they may rely on the planning authorities to guide them.

One large operator bases its predictions on the principles of BS5228 but uses its own measurements of noise levels of specific activities rather than the typical values quoted in BS5228. This allows the company to benefit from noise data that is specific to the machinery to be used, where this is quieter than the "typical" machines quoted in BS5228. As an example, the company has noted that machinery manufactured by Volvo is particularly quiet in operation. This operator considers that the noise levels of BS5228 tend to be more appropriate to older designs which may not incorporate the additional silencing features now available.

British Coal is at present of the opinion that the "best predictive achievement to date is based on a practical approach and experience of similar site operations in comparable conditions". This is the result of its "Opencast Noise Monitoring Programme" which was set up in November 1980 and was concluded in September 1982. As part of the monitoring programme, three different prediction methods were evaluated, two of which had been developed within the Opencast Executive and one by a noise consultant. Unfortunately the details of the three methods have not been made available, but the Opencast Executive reports that they all tended to overpredict and were therefore considered to be unreliable. They used input data which had been measured on the actual working sites and produced predictions which tended to be too high by as much as 12 dB L_{Aeq}. Subsequent work by the Opencast Executive is reported to have reduced this error to typically 5 or 6 dB(A).

The predictions made for small operators, usually by consultants, have not been made available to this study for reasons of confidentiality. However it is understood that these are normally based on the principles of BS5228.

3.3.4 Summary of current practice

To summarise, there are distinct variations in the use of noise prediction methods by mineral planning authorities and site operators. Most make use of BS5228, but the standard is applied in

9

such a variety of ways that there is no coherent approach across the country. Only a few mineral planning authorities have wide experience of predicting noise from surface mineral workings. A few have experience limited to specific resources such as sand and gravel, but the majority have little or no relevant experience.

3.4   Noise monitoring

Both mineral planning authorities and site operators have an interest in monitoring the noise produced by surface mineral workings, and in determining whether that noise is within any limit imposed as a planning condition. Limits are specified a variety of ways. For example they may specify the number and location of monitoring points, the units in which measurements are to be made, and the period or duration of those measurements. A typical requirement might be for measurements of 8 hour L_{Aeq} at unspecified points on the site boundary. Within considerable variation, three basic approaches are currently used, and these are discussed below.

3.4.1 Semi-permanent monitoring of overall site noise

Semi-permanent monitoring stations, which continuously measure and record the sound level at a certain point, are used by some larger operators but are rarely a specific requirement imposed by mineral planning authorities. Such systems are necessarily sophisticated and expensive.

British Coal undertakes fairly extensive noise monitoring. A particular reason is that its sites are worked by contractors on whom it imposes noise limits which reflect the limits contained in the planning conditions. British Coal is held responsible by the local authorities for any excessive noise, so it needs to ensure that contractors comply with the noise limits.

A basic semi-permanent noise monitoring system typically contains a weatherproof microphone with facilities for remote calibration and for heating to prevent the microphone being affected by

10

condensation. The signal from the microphone is fed to an analysis and logging system which will store a continuous record of one or more noise variables (eg L_{Aeq}, L_{max}, L_{10} and L_{90}).

The basic system may be extended in several ways. Several microphones distributed across a site may be used with a single analysis system, their outputs being sampled in rotation. Data from an anemometer may be fed in parallel with the noise signal, facilitating interpretation of the recorded noise level by permitting comparison with wind speed and direction. Occasionally a tape recorder may be linked to the analysis system, automatically triggered to record for a short time if the noise exceeds a preset level. This may help to identify the source of particularly high levels of noise. Such sophistication does however increase the risk of technical problems.

A common problem is the recording of high noise levels associated with sources such as low-flying aircraft which, although they may be identified by a tape recording, may give rise to misleading results. Vandalism to equipment, which is left unattended in the open, can also occur. There are technical problems associated with transmitting signals from the microphone to the analyser, which may be a few miles apart. Finally, the environmental conditions to which equipment is exposed over long periods of time requires very robust and reliable systems, and some failures are almost inevitable.

With perseverence and attention to detail, it is possible to produce an adequate monitoring system. But some site operators are known to have given up on a long-term monitoring system after continued operational problems, and have instead opted for occasional monitoring techniques.

3.4.2 Occasional monitoring of overall site noise

Occasional monitoring using portable equipment is far more common than the use of semi-permanent monitoring stations. Operators may use this approach on a regular scheduled programme. However, local authorities tend to act in pursuance of their obligations under the Control of Pollution Act following a complaint.

Where occasional monitoring is used to check compliance with a planning condition, measurement locations may have been defined. Otherwise, the locations will be at representative points on the site boundary, or at the location from which the complaint originates.

For occasional monitoring, the instrumentation need not be as sophisticated and expensive, nor quite as robust, as that required for continuous monitoring. Portable instruments are suitable. Instruments will normally be left unattended for 8 or 12 hours at a single location depending on the monitoring period specified in the planning consent. Manned measurement has the advantage that occasional noise from extraneous or irrelevant sources can be excluded, but it is not universal practice for prolonged monitoring as it is expensive in terms of manpower. Even unmanned monitoring may require considerable staff-time to set up and collect the equipment, with a risk that crucial results may be lost through equipment failure during the unattended period.

Consequently, there is some pressure for a shorter monitoring period which would permit continuous manning together with the possibility of covering several locations in one day.

Occasional monitoring is essentially a sampling process: and samples have to be sufficent in duration and number to enable the underlying values to be determined with acceptable reliability. There is no guidance in BS5228, or any other convenient reference, on what constitutes 'sufficient' sampling. However, there is some evidence that short samples taken over a number of days may be more reliable than longer samples on few days. This problem is addressed in Section 4.2.

It could be argued that occasional monitoring does not meet the needs of Environmental Health Officers in responding to complaints, since by the time a complaint can be acted upon, the incident to which it relates is in the past, and therefore unmeasurable. However, this argument assumes that the incident is not recurrent, in which case its impact on the public would be limited.

Site operators, if they do not have a permanent monitoring system, may take occasional noise measurements at the site boundary to satisfy themselves that they are working within the limits imposed on them. Their reasons for monitoring may also include an element of public relations, as they will be seen to be taking positive action to control noise.

3.4.3 Noise emissions of plant and equipment

It is rare for planning conditions to specify noise requirements in terms of specific limits for items of machinery, so monitoring of machinery noise for the purpose of verifying compliance with the planning conditions is uncommon. However some site operators have a policy of making regular checks of the noise levels of their machinery, to ensure that items such as silencers are functioning properly.

Typically, the noise level is measured at the front, back and two sides of the machine, with the engine idling. Any discrepancy between the measured levels and the established normal levels is investigated and remedied.

The measurement methods used by various operators vary in their detail. In one case, the checks on noise emissions from individual items of plant were part of a process intended to ensure that site boundary limits were not exceeded. Of course this is easier when a small range and quantity of plant is used within a limited area. Whatever system is used, any programme of diagnosis and remedial maintenance will help to control the site boundary levels.

3.4.4 Facilities available to local authorities

Local authorities deal with noise matters both at county and at borough or district level. The distribution of responsibilities between the two depends to some extent on the expertise available. Whilst all county authorities have a planning department, very few of these departments have their own noise expertise and so they must seek other sources of guidance when necessary.

13

A number of county authorities have their own environmental health departments which advise the planning department on noise matters. Such departments usually have a noise specialist who can undertake the necessary calculations and assessments.

Authorities which do not have their own environmental health departments may have personnel in the Highways or Surveyor's departments who can deal with noise problems. However, the most common source of advice is from borough or district environmental health departments. These departments are, in any case, responsible for dealing with complaints from the public and they can usually undertake noise monitoring when necessary. Since they must deal with all types of environmental problem, not just noise, their ability to undertake detailed noise calculations can be limited both in terms of time and specialist knowledge. However, authorities which regularly deal with noise problems do have the relevant experience, and there is some degree of pooling of resources between authorities. The use of outside consultants is relatively infrequent.

Environmental health officers typically have access to equipment such as an environmental noise analyser which will give direct measurements of the common measures such as L_{Aeq}, L_{10}, L_{90} and maximum noise level. One Borough Council has a Range Rover fitted with noise measuring equipment, which it uses primarily for monitoring opencast coal site noise; this level of equipment is, however, exceptional amongst local authorities.

The general situation is seen to be one of adequate facilties to deal with the common types of noise measurement and assessment, but extensive or long-term monitoring and assessment will be beyond the in-house capabilities of most authorities.

3.5 Noise abatement measures

Noise abatement measures fall into three broad categories. Noise may be:
- controlled at source
- controlled between the source and receiver
- controlled by limiting the hours of operation

3.5.1 Control at source

The control of noise at source is achieved by the use of quiet models and types of machinery, perhaps with special silencing systems, or by using quieter methods of working. In opencast mining, the extensive and growing use of electrically operated (instead of diesel powered) machinery is a welcome trend in this direction. Disappointingly, an approach to most of the earthmoving and mining equipment manufacturers to discuss their work on noise control met, with the exception of Volvo, an unenthusiastic response. Perhaps operators do not place a high priority on noise emissions when evaluating alternative equipment, and manufacturers see no evidence of a demand for quieter equipment. Of course the introduction of EEC directives (see Appendix A) may change this situation.

Noise emissions from mobile plant may also be controlled at source by reducing the speed at which it travels. For example "sleeping policemen" are in use at a sand and gravel quarry in Kent, restricting the speed of lorries on a private approach road.

3.5.2 Control of propagation

Controlling the propagation of sound between source and receiver is essentially a question of using distance or barriers. Where equipment is fixed, walls or heavy fences can be used as barriers (such as in the Kent quarry mentioned above). The location of fixed plant within the site is constrained by the distribution of the mineral reserves, but within those contraints there can be alternatives with greater or lesser impact on neighbouring properties. The location of fixed plant is usually decided by the site operator rather than being imposed by the mineral planning authority.

15

3.5.3 Baffle mounds

Baffle mounds are the most common way to control the propagation of noise by placing a physical barrier between source and receiver. The result, provided the mound is properly located and of sufficient height, is typically a reduction of 10dB(A).

Baffle mounds are normally constructed just inside the site boundary with soil or overburden taken from within the site, to a height of 5m. Much higher mounds may be constructed if the site operator is using the mound as his main overburden dump, subject to any restrictions on the visual intrusion of the mound: these will produce somewhat greater noise reductions. However, where a baffle mound is constructed mainly as a noise control measure it rarely exceeds 5m, as a law of diminishing returns operates, and there may be a reluctance to sacrifice the working area of the site to accommodate the larger base area of a higher mound.

Paradoxically, baffle mounds not only control noise, but are themselves a source of noise during construction. The noise disturbance is aggravated by three facts. Firstly, they are necessarily located closer to noise sensitive properties than subsequent site activities; secondly, earth moving equipment has to operate in direct line of sight to those properties; and thirdly, the baffle mounds are constructed at an early stage, before residents have been able to adapt to the presence of the site and when resentment to its existence may be strongest. As a consequence baffle mounds tend to be constructed as quickly as possible, often within a two week period.

3.5.4 Self-screening

The working face itself can constitute a noise barrier. By arranging the direction of work so that the site machinery tends to operate at the base of the working face, with the noise sensitive properties behind the face and therefore shielded by it, a considerable reduction in the noise level can sometimes be achieved.

16

The exact reduction in noise level depends on the relative heights and distances of the machinery, working face and noise sensitive properties. Such a change in work practices was made at a Fullers Earth quarry in Bedfordshire, where the proposed direction of working was reversed in order to reduce noise nuisance.

3.5.5 Hours of working

One of the most effective means of noise control is to restrict the hours of working. For sand, gravel and hard rock sites it is normal for work to be limited to daytime hours, which are normally taken to be 7am to 7pm, but vary slightly according to local practice. Work is not permitted on Sundays and public holidays. Nevertheless, a noise nuisance can be caused in the very early morning at such sites. This arises from empty lorries arriving at the site early, ready to be loaded as soon as it opens, thereby using local roads at times when people expect to be able to sleep. Attempts to stop this practice by forbidding early arrival have failed, because lorries then wait at a convenient spot a mile or so away.

For opencast coal sites, where the scale of the operations is considerably larger and with much greater capital investment, economic considerations may require night-time working to achieve viable production levels, although many sites do not operate at night. Where night-time working takes place, the noise limit is normally lower than for the day-time; examples of limits are given in section 3.6 of this report.

At night, lower noise levels are achieved by changing the work pattern. The movement of overburden continues, but the extraction of coal ceases. This means that all the work is contained within the site, with no movements of coal lorries or other forms of coal transport in the surrounding area. The night-time use of dump trucks, which are a major source of noise, varies from site to site, but draglines are normally in full-time use. Complaints about noise at night from opencast sites tend to relate to the clanking of the dragline chains and bucket.

3.6   Planning controls

In the exercise of their duty, mineral planning authorities may impose, or agree with operators, specific conditions intended to limit the noise nuisance from surface mineral workings. Five approaches can be identified from current practice:

- to identify the specific items of plant and equipment which are sources of a potential noise problem, and impose controls on their noise emissions.

- to specify a noise level, at the site boundary, that must not be exceeded.

- to specify a noise level, at a noise-sensitive property, that must not be exceeded.

- to require that the operator adopts 'best practicable means' to minimise the noise nuisance caused by his operations.

- to limit hours of operation, usually to protect residental areas from noise-induced sleep disturbance.

The five approaches are discussed separately below, but are frequently used in parallel.

3.6.1 Limiting the noise emissions of plant

Currently, noise limits are seldom imposed directly on individual items of machinery through the planning conditions. The manpower required to make regular checks on machinery noise levels precludes the local authorities from undertaking the enforcement of such a condition. The availability of equipment, and of a suitable flat and quiet measuring site also limits the use of this approach.

One case where noise limits have been set for the machinery itself is at the Ashfordby coal mine in Leicestershire. Under the permission granted in 1983 the following condition was included:

18

"Except as otherwise agreed by the County Planning Authority, no individual item of plant, equipment or machinery, (fixed or mobile, and permanent or temporary) nor any vehicle shall at any time emit a noise which, when measured at a distance of 5 metres in any direction from the item of plant, equipment or machinery (or from an external wall if the item of plant equipment or machinery is enclosed within a building) or from the vehicle, exceeds a level of 93 dB(A) or (if less) the maximum level of noise permitted by the Motor Vehicles (Construction and Use) Regulations 1978 (as amended or replaced by similar provisions) in respect of a goods vehicle exceeding 7.5 tonnes gross weight. For the purposes of this condition, a representative of the County Planning Authority shall be allowed access to the surface application site at all times in order to measure noise levels".

Some authorities will encourage an operator to use the quietest available make and type of equipment, and may specify particular machinery types to be used. This is known to have occurred in particular at a sand and gravel site in East Sussex. This approach requires considerable research to be carried out by the authority, in order to compare the different manufacturers' products. Although various British and International Standards are being prepared to standardise noise test methods on construction machinery, it is at present difficult to obtain directly comparable noise data from manufacturers since the methods of test vary or may not be relevant to normal operating conditions. This makes the task of establishing the quietest machinery available a relatively complex matter and requires staff with expertise in acoustics. However, recent EC directives now require type-testing and noise certification of "construction plant," which includes many items used in surface mineral workings, and should help to encourage the adoption of quieter plant.

One limitation of this approach is that the in-use noise emission of machinery is dependent not only on its design, but also on the quality of its maintenance. A poorly maintained machine can make significantly more noise than the same machine in good condition, and often the extra noise is of a particularly annoying character, such as squeaky bearings or ineffective exhaust silencing. A well organised site operator will, as a matter of course, ensure his machinery is in good order if he owns it, in order to prolong its working life, but as machinery is often hired, the incentive for preventative maintenance is not universal.

However, it is generally impracticable to require maintenance schedules (as distinct from times at which maintenance work is permitted) or maintenance testing as part of planning conditions: maintenance depends on the amount of use of the plant; furthermore, planning authorities neither have the expertise to devise such conditions nor the manpower to enforce them. Nevertheless, it is recognised that operators should be encouraged to undertake a programme of preventative maintenance of plant equipment.

Site operators naturally want their work methods to be constrained as little as possible by planning conditions. They do not want to have specific makes and models of equipment imposed on them by the mineral planning authority, but would prefer any restriction on machinery type to be in the form of generalised constraints which might include a maximum sound power level. The mineral planning authority should not in any case specify machinery items because it does not hold responsibility for factors such as safety or reliability. In practice, the mineral planning authority will at most sanction machinery makes and models proposed by the site operator.

It should not be assumed that the question of noise will be resolved by a planning condition which specifies the maximum machinery noise levels. This type of condition gives no guarantee that noise levels will be acceptable at properties near to the site, since these are highly dependent on the distance between the machine and the properties, and on the presence of barriers.

3.6.2 Noise limits at the site boundary

3.6.2.1 Monitoring locations

A more common approach to the control of noise nuisance by planning conditions is for the mineral planning authority to set a noise limit at the site boundary.

Such an approach could be ambiguous in the content of mineral extraction where operations are often partly or wholly screened, either by the edge of the excavation or by a baffle mound. Clearly, very different readings will be obtained at locations in the acoustic shadow of a baffle mound compared with unscreened locations. Secondly, high readings will be obtained when plant is working close to the monitoring position, compared with readings when it is working at a more distant part of the site. Given the large size of many opencast sites, which can be more than 2km across, the working position has a dramatic effect on the monitored noise level, and can vary considerably from day to day.

Both of these factors will have a greater effect at the site boundary than at more distant points, where people are actually living.

This need not be a difficulty provided the precise monitoring locations are clearly defined in relation to working positions and any acoustic screening in the vicinity. The noise limit must also take such screening into account, together with the reduction in noise over the distance intervening between the monitoring location and noise-sensitive locations. This is discussed in greater detail in Section 4.4.

3.6.2.2 Noise limit levels

Ideally, site boundary noise limits would be set to ensure that the site operator works within the noise levels which have been confirmed as acceptable for the local environment. In practice

21

the present selection of a limit seems to be based on precedent rather than analysis of a site, with 57 dB(A) being popular. This limit probably originates from the Flowers Commission Report which cites the Butterwell opencast site noise limit of 57 dB(A): if so, it is a misuse of a limit which was intended to apply at 1 metre from noise sensitive buildings.

Where L_{Aeq} is used, it is becoming very common for a limit of 65 dB(A) over 12 hours at the site boundary to applied, especially to open-cast sites. This is notwithstanding the fact that such a blanket approach ignores the distance of sensitive locations from the site and the relative effectiveness of screening at the monitoring point compared with the sensitve locations.

3.6.3 Noise limits at noise-sensitive properties

Since the primary objective is to control the exposure of noise-sensitive properties, it is not surprising to find that the most common approach adopted by mineral planning authorities is to define a noise limit at the facade of such properties.

3.6.3.1 BS4142

Many authorities base their selection of an appropriate noise limit on British Standard BS4142 "Method of rating industrial noise affecting mixed residential and industrial areas". In simple terms, BS4142 rates the likelihood of complaints in terms of how far the intruding noise is above or below the background noise.

However, it is important to recognise that BS4142 does not claim to be a method of setting noise criteria even for industrial installations. It is merely a tool for assessing the likelihood of complaints. Although a BS4142 rating may be of interest when determining an application for a minerals development, it can only be one of a number of factors to be considered. This is because mineral developments differ in many respects from a fixed industrial site, particularly in terms of choice over location, life-span and variability of the noise.

Minerals developments generally have a short life-span. The noise can be very variable, being highest during soil-stripping and some tipping operations. At these times, it may well be desirable to permit much higher noise levels than would be acceptable for a fixed factory installation (although higher levels are frequently permitted during the construction phase of a factory) otherwise mineral reserves may be unnecessarily sterilized, or extraction costs may become unecomonically high. Furthermore, the setting of a low criterion may unnecessarily protract the extraction operation, which may not be in the best interests of the local population.

Futhermore, it would not be easy to apply BS4142 in a meaningful way to a minerals site. This is because the method (as it currently stands) assumes that the noise output is at a steady, well-defined level. This is reasonable for a factory, but unrealistic for a minerals site. BS4142 would have to be applied separately to different operations within the life-cycle of the site and a judgment would need to be made if some operations were deemed to cause complaints whilst others were found not to do so.

It should be emphasised that the variability of noise which causes difficulty is not the short-term variation within, say, a working day, which the proposed adoption of LAeq would largely resolve, but the longer weekly and monthly variation as the site is worked.

For these reasons, it is inappropriate to use BS4142 on its own when determining minerals applications. Such ratings provide useful information on the amount of noise generated by a site, but they only show part of the picture. At present, the setting of a criterion must be partly a value judgment which should include such factors as the absolute noise level, times, durations, cost and practicability of reducing the noise, value of the site, effect on its viability, and the trade-off between noise limits and the lifetime of the site.

The deficiencies of BS4142 when applied to surface mineral workings are widely recognised by planners, and the Opencast Executive positively discourages its application to opencast coal mines. It continues in use largely because there is no other agreed quantitative method for setting appropriate limits.

3.6.3.2 BS5228

BS5228, "Noise Control on Construction and Open Sites", does comment on the criteria to be considered in setting noise control targets, and indeed introduces its discussion with the comment:

"It is not possible to provide detailed guidance for determining whether or not noise from a site will constitute a problem in a particular situation".

3.6.3.3 Cheshire County Council guidelines

Cheshire County Council has developed a method of setting L_{Aeq} noise limits at the facade of noise-sensitive properties which is intended for any new industrial or commercial development. It has been used in a number of cases for sand and gravel extraction sites, and has reportedly been successful in reducing the number of complaints to virtually nil.

In this method, the area surrounding a proposed development is categorised according to its ability to tolerate an increase in noise level: Category A cannot accept any increase in noise, Category B can accept marginal increases, and Category C can accept significant increases. There is some element of value judgement in the assignment of the category for a particular area: a decision has to be made as to how much noise increase an area can accept. Having done so, the existing background noise level (L_{90}) is measured. The noise limit is then set according to the rule system below:

Category	Example Area	Noise Limit in L_{Aeq} at facade of Noise Sensitive Property
A	100% Residential	L_{90} less 10
B	Quiet rural areas with scattered housing; mixed residential and industrial.	L_{90} plus 5
C	100% Industrial, or agricultural land.	No limit

Where the proposed noise source has a significant tonal, impulsive or irregular character the noise limit is to be reduced by 5 units.

Where appropriate, the background noise level is measured during the daytime, in the evening, and at night; different limits are set for each period.

The Cheshire method has been in use since 1980, and has been modified in some details. For example where the existing L_{Aeq} noise level at the noise sensitive property is close to the intended L_{Aeq} limit, it would be difficult to measure the intruding noise with any certainty unless this is greatly in excess of the limit. Therefore, a site boundary value may be fixed by calculation, such that if the site boundary value is not exceeded, the noise limit at the noise-sensitive properties will also not be exceeded. (The factors making a site boundary limit easier to enforce are discussed in Section 4.3.2).

Cheshire County Council recognises that there can be a problem in Category B areas with low L_{90} values. A measured L_{90} value of 20 dB(A) would limit new sources to 25 dB(A) L_{Aeq} (1 hr), which is thought by Cheshire to be too restrictive. It is probable that a cut-off will be introduced into the rule system, so that no Category B limit will be more stringent than 30 or 35 dB(A) L_{Aeq} (1 hr).

The Cheshire County Council system is strict, even onerous. Given that L_{eq} values are typically 5 dB higher than L_{90}, it effectively limits new noise to 15 dB(A) below existing levels in residential areas, and to existing levels in rural areas. It is perhaps to be expected that complaints would not arise in such circumstances but, applied to surface mineral workings, could be overly and unnecessarily restrictive.

3.6.3.4 Authorisations at open cast sites

Opencast coal sites tend to be subject to limits on the L_{Aeq} which have been set with reference to past case histories rather than to the background noise conditions prevailing at the site in question. The limits appear to be similar for most opencast coal sites, and their earliest form is that used in the Butterwell authorisation of 1975, which when revised in 1977 stated:

"a) between 2200 hours on any day and 0600 hours on the following day the equivalent continuous sound level (L_{eq}) attributable to the authorised operations during this period or during such part of each shift (if more than one) as is worked between those hours at any noise-sensitive building outside the site shall not be more than 50 dB(A) and the maximum noise level so attributable at any such building shall not be more than 60 dB(A); and

b) between 0600 hours and 2200 hours on any day the equivalent continuous sound level (L_{eq}) during such part of each shift as is worked between those hours at any noise-sensitive building outside the site shall not be more than 57 dB(A) and the maximum noise level at any such building (excluding noise attributable to blasting) shall not be more than 70 dB(A)."

The construction and removal of baffle mounds is specifically excluded from the above limits. During the 20 working days allowed for their construction and 30 for their removal the above limits can be exceeded.

In the Butterwell conditions, a noise sensitive building may be a dwelling, but it could also be a hospital, school, or place of worship, or indeed any other building type which is likely to be affected by an increase in noise.

Recent consents have shown wide variations on this theme. Generally, there are daytime, evening and night-time periods: typically daytime working is from 0700 to 1900 Monday to Friday, 0700 to 1300 on Saturday; evening is 1900 to 2200 Monday to Friday; and night-time levels apply at other times, including Sundays.

Noise limits are typically either set at the site boundary, at noise-sensitive properties, or both.

Where a boundary limit is set, this is usually up to 65 dB(A) L_{Aeq} at the site boundary for day-time working, ranging through intermediate levels for evening periods, down as low as 40 dB(A) for some night-time limits.

There is usually some provision for a limited amount of "noisy" work, for which day-time limits are relaxed.

Interestingly, where limits are set at noise sensitive properties, these also range from 65 dB(A) (free-field) downwards for daytime levels, with correspondingly lower night-time levels, for example 45 dB(A). It is noted that in some of the recent permissions, there seems to be little recognition that it should be possible to achieve lower noise levels because of the distance between the site and the noise-sensitive property: the limit looks as though it has been chosen as much to permit the working of the site as to protect the property concerned.

The monitoring period in recent permissions generally corresponds to the working period. In one case, this requires monitoring over periods of 3,5,6,9,10 and 12 hours, depending on the activity and the time of occurrence.

In Scotland there are no noise limits set at coal sites.

3.6.3.5 Authorisations at other sites.

Noise limits at 1m outside "any building used for human habitation" were set in the planning conditions at a tungsten and tin mine in Devon. The limits for L_{Aeq} (1 hour) were 50 dB(A) daytime, 45 dB(A) evenings, and 40 dB(A) at other times including Sundays and Public Holidays.

On occasions an application is made to extend an existing mineral working to include previously unworked land. In such cases some authorities such as Bedfordshire County Council have imposed a condition that the L_{Aeq} levels produced by the existing site at noise-sensitive properties shall not be increased by the extension of the site.

It is clear that even amongst mineral planning authorities who agree on using noise limits defined at noise-sensitive properties, there is considerable variation not only in the actual limits, but also in the method by which such limits should be determined.

3.6.4 Best practicable means

3.6.4.1 Application to surface mineral workings

Another approach which avoids the setting of specific noise limits altogether is to require via a planning condition that the operator adopt the "best practicable means" to mimimise the noise produced.

The use of "best practicable means" as a method of controlling environmental noise arose initially from the Control of Pollution Act 1974 Section 58 (5). This states that "in respect of a noise caused in the course of trade or business, it shall be a defence

28

to prove that the best practicable means have been used for preventing, or for counteracting the effect of the noise". Section 72 defines "practicable" and details the limits of application of best practicable means.

However, the use of best practicable means in the Control of Pollution Act is in a different context from its use as a planning condition. In the Control of Pollution Act, it is a means by which someone being prosecuted for causing a noise nuisance can make a defence on the grounds that they are doing everything that can reasonably be expected to minimise the nuisance. It is however implied under the Act that "best practicable means" need only be applied if a nuisance would otherwise be caused. When the best practicable means are required in a planning condition, the site operator is expected to adopt them whether or not he would otherwise cause a nuisance. Rather than being a form of defence for the operator, it has become a condition to which he must adhere.

A "Best Practicable Means" requirement has in a few cases been the sole condition of a planning consent. Supplementary restraints on the methods and times of work, the use of particular noise reduction techniques, or other detailed conditions may be additionally imposed.

For example, Northumberland County Council stated in a permission for a coal site that "All reasonable steps shall be taken to minimise noise from vehicles and machinery and in particular efficient silencers shall be fitted to and used by all vehicles and machinery on the site". In most cases however the best practicable means condition is used in combination with some form of noise limit, whether at the site boundary or at nearby properties.

3.6.4.2 Legal arguments against use as planning condition

The legal arguments against the use of 'best practicable means' as a planning condition were succinctly stated by Mr Gerrard Ryan QC appearing for Derbyshire County Council in the Appeal by the NCB Opencast Executive against refusal of permission for the development of the Kirk Site.

"It is well established that one characteristic of a planning condition is that it must be sufficiently certain in its operation for enforcement of its provisions to be carried out if the condition is breached (Fawcett v Bucks CC 1961 AC 636; 1960 3 AER 503). Another way of putting the proposition is that a condition is void for uncertainty if it can be given no sensible or ascertainable meaning. It is also the case that a condition is imposed to last for the duration of a permission. The reasons for uncertainty arising from a "best practicable means" condition are:

a) There is no certainty as to what constitutes 'best practicable means' at any time: one party may be advised that System A should be employed; another that it should be System B. Such matters can only be resolved by the decision of a court or an arbitrator (which explains why 'best practicable means' may be used as a defence to a breach of a duty of care at common law or by statute). 'Best practicable means' carries within it the germ of dispute.

b) A system or mechanism found to constitute 'best practicable means' at one date may be overtaken by another system or mechanism at a later date. Thus the basis for enforcement might vary from time to time: that is inherently uncertain.

c) 'Best practicable means' carries an element of economy of investment in whatever system or mechanism is employed. The enforcement of a planning condition cannot properly be made to depend on such a criterion: the criterion is itself incapable of resolution without an effective measure of arbitration to ascertain what the best practicable means is.

d) M J Shanley v Secretary of State (DCC 116) may be used as an illustration by analogy. There, the obligation, by condition, to give 'the first opportunity to local people' to buy houses was unsupported by an reference to the mechanism whereby this was to be secured. Similarly there is no way of providing by definition for what should constitute 'best practicable means' on account of its variable and argumentative nature as a concept. A requirement which lacks a mechanism enabling a local planning authority to ascertain whether it is being met is a requirement which, expressed as a condition, is void."

The Inspector accepted these arguments, and in the final paragraph of his letter to the Secretary of State said:

"The Board show a strong preference for the 'best practicable means' type of condition. It has obviously been widely applied in the past. I can see that it has some superficial attraction because it lets in technological innovations which can progressively afford more environmental protection to surrounding areas. However, the legal submissions by leading counsel, which have been reported in full in paragraph ... above, make a compelling case against the use of this type of condition."

Those who advocate the use of "best practicable means" as the sole noise condition point to the difficulties associated with administering noise limits to support their argument. In the setting of limits there may be considerable difficulty in selecting a limit which is both feasible for the site operator to work within and low enough to ensure that no noise nuisance is caused, and in the monitoring of limits there are considerable demands made on the time of local authority staff and on equipment.

A "best practicable means" requirement is inadequate both from a practical and a legal point of view. It does not address the problem of whether a proposed site, even when all available means to reduce noise have been taken, will be environmentally acceptable. Only by setting a noise limit, combined with an investigation of whether the site could work within such a limit, can this important question be answered.

3.6.5 Limiting hours of operation

Any noise limit which differs for different times of day implies that certain operations, or combinations of operations, are allowed at some times but not at others.

Previous sections have given a number of examples in which hours of operation have been specified, and separate discussion is unnecessary.

3.7   Liaison committees

Resentment is the almost inevitable reaction when a surface mineral site starts operating near an established community. However the quality of the continuing relationship between site operators and local residents is to a considerable extent dependent on the operator being seen to take active measures to reduce noise and other nuisances.

One way in which good relations can be fostered, which is now frequently used in the context of opencast coal workings, is to establish a local liaison committee. The committee includes representatives of the site operators, the contractor, local authorities and residents. In the early stages of a site's development the committee meets frequently, perhaps monthly, but later meetings become less frequent.

The meetings provide a forum for the public to explain its concerns directly to the site operator, and for the site operator in turn to explain and discuss the working of the site. If a particularly annoying process is expected to be carried out in the near future, such as the building of baffle banks, then this can be raised at the meeting and the reasons for it explained.

The liaison committee does not replace the continuing role of the Mineral Planning Authority to enforce the planning conditions nor that of the Environmental Health Officer, who must still deal with individual complaints, though it may facilitate their work by informing them of the general level of feeling within a community and alerting them to potential problems.

4.0 RESEARCH STUDIES

The research studies were directed along four main avenues:-

- Noise prediction techniques
- Noise monitoring methods
- Community response to noise
- Methods of setting noise limits

The main findings were:-

- the BS5228 prediction method provides a good basis for calculating noise emission from surface mineral workings;
- noise monitoring should be undertaken at the site boundary;
- community response studies indicate that best current practice can keep noise to levels which are acceptable to the community at large, although this will not entirely eliminate complaints;
- noise limits should be designed to control the exposure of noise-sensitive properties;
- the link between controlling exposure at sensitive properties whilst monitoring at the site boundary can be made through the noise calculation method.

4.1 Noise prediction methodology

4.1.1 Introduction

British Standard BS5228 "Noise control on construction and open sites" provides the foundation for all prediction methods currently used for minerals sites. It is based on simple, well-proven acoustics principles but consciously ignores certain factors such as ground attenuation (by vegetation, etc) and meteorological conditions (particularly wind direction). It has a simplified approach to barrier screening. Furthermore, it provides limited guidance on practical application to large and complex sites, particularly those having a network of haul roads.

No investigations into its accuracy for surface minerals workings were found in published literature, but British Coal in particular suggested that it over-predicted noise levels.

For effective design and noise control of minerals sites, it is essential to have an accurate and reliable prediction method, and therefore an investigation was undertaken to verify and, if possible, improve the existing methodology.

Techniques for dealing with the noise propagation factors omitted from BS5228 can be found in other prediction methods currently used in the UK. Two such methods are "Calculation of Road Traffic Noise 1988" (CRTN) (Department of Transport) and CONCAWE (developed for the oil and petrochemical industry).

The study, which included an investigation into the merits of these additional techniques, is fully reported in Appendix B: the approach and findings are summarised here.

4.1.2 Comparative studies

A comprehensive noise measurement study was made at four minerals workings, namely two opencast coal sites, a sand and gravel pit and a limestone quarry. A total of 18 measurement positions were used in the analysis.

The measured sound power levels for the main items of plant, an up-to-date contour map of the site, measured daily L_{eq} values at various points within and outside the site, and detailed information on the movements and times of work of all machinery were obtained for each site. By using such detailed data, the study was expected to indicate what prediction accuracy each of the various techniques could achieve. It was, of course, recognised that such detail would not always be available in practice.

4.1.3 Results

The study showed that, contrary to expectations, BS5228 as it stands gave very good prediction accuracy provided the contribution from each haul road was corrected as described in Appendix B for the angle of view it subtended at the receiver. The basic method had a slight tendency to over-predict which was reduced by adding in a soft ground correction derived from the CONCAWE approach. With this additional correction, the correlation coefficient was r = 0.85, with a slope of 0.95 and intercept of 4.5.

It was found that the CRTN soft ground attenuation was too great when extrapolated to the large distances (up to 2km) involved in this study.

It was interesting to note that the addition of the sophisticated CRTN or CONCAWE barrier correction unexpectedly worsened the prediction accuracy. These provide for greater amounts of barrier attenuation than the 10 dB(A) maximum given by BS5228. The effect has not been explained but could be due to "canyon effect" (ie reflection of sound between the rock faces) which reduces the effectiveness of barriers.

Finally, the meteorological correction from CONCAWE introduced a large scatter into the results. This correction is very sensitive to small variations in meteorological conditions, especially wind direction, leading to instability which is unacceptable in a planning tool.

More stable results are obtained with a positive wind component (such as assumed by CRTN). In such conditions, both soft ground and barrier effects are reduced, which increases the measured noise level. This may be a factor in explaining the good performance of the basic method.

4.1.4 Prediction at the early planning stage

The investigation of a very simple prediction method based on the noise levels likely to be produced by dump trucks, applied to opencast coal, showed surprisingly good results. The method might therefore be used to gain an initial impression of the noise levels at the early planning stage, before sufficient information becomes available to make more detailed calculations. This method is fully described in Appendix B.

4.1.5 Conclusions on noise prediction methodology

Within the limits of this research, the basic BS5228 prediction method gives good prediction accuracy provided:

(a) Sound power levels are obtained for the actual plant in use on the site;

(b) The correction shown in Appendix B is applied to Haul roads which subtend less than 180 degrees at the calculation point.

(c) The prediction accuracy can be further improved by making the alternative correction (shown in Appendix B) for soft ground attenuation when this is greater than the barrier correction. A refinement to the relatively coarse barrier correction did not improve prediction accuracy: this point requires further research.

4.2   Monitoring

4.2.1 Introduction

The principal questions addressed by this research are: where should monitoring take place, and over what time period? It is recommended that monitoring should take place at locations stipulated in the planning consent which should generally be at the site boundary. Monitoring for compliance with planning conditions should be made over periods of one or more hours, depending on how critical the result is found to be, on typical working days, using attended precision measuring instruments.

4.2.2 Equipment

The sound level meter should be at least Type 1 (precision grade) as defined by BS5969 (1981), and be able to measure L_{Aeq}. It is also highly desirable for the equipment to be rainproof so that it may be used outside without fear of damage from the weather. It should be possible to mount the microphone at a height of 1.5m above ground level, for example on a tripod, and the microphone should be covered with a windshield.

4.2.3 Monitoring location

There are two distinct possibilities for the location of the monitoring system: the site boundary and the affected property. Experience from the monitoring fieldwork suggests that measurements at affected properties only give a representative evaluation of the site's noise if the prevailing noise from other sources is exceptionally low. Measurements taken within or close to the site, provided they are not disproportionately close to any one noise source, have by contrast been shown to be reliable indicators of the site's overall noise.

Monitoring at the affected property has the attraction, both to the enforcement agency and to the resident, of measuring the noise which is actually heard. As the research has shown, noise levels from most sites are close to the ambient noise level and current measurement techniques lack the discriminatory power of the human ear to detect the intruding noise in such situations.

Apart from acoustical resons, there could be legal difficulties in stipulating noise control points which are on a third party's private property, as access would be needed at all times.

Consequently, it is recommended that monitoring should only be carried out at affected properties to check on cases where nuisance is alleged: it should not be used as a means of controlling noise nor testing for compliance with planning conditions.

Monitoring at the site boundary is more reliable provided the noise control points are correctly selected. In particular, the noise control points:

- should be related to the general location of noise-sensitive areas.
- should not be unduly affected by unrelated noise such as traffic on public roads.
- should not be in the acoustic "shadow" of a baffle mound (they should be on top of any such mound).
- should not be disproportionately close to any one noise source unless this is taken into account when setting the noise control level.
- should be written into the planning consent.

The noise control levels should be related to noise at sensitive properties by calculation, using the analytical methods described in Section 4.1.

4.2.4   Noise monitoring procedure

The equivalent continuous noise level, L_{Aeq} is the recommended unit of measurement. It is well-established in the measurement of noise from surface mineral workings, and is likely to be adopted in the revised BS4142 procedure for rating industrial noise. It has many practical advantages over other units and can be measured by a number of commercially available sound level meters. Its main disadvantage, a sensitivity to short periods of high-level intruding noise, can be overcome by manning the monitoring sessions. This need not be onerous provided a suitable sampling procedure can be devised, and provided monitoring is not required over extended periods.

This research indicates a suitable sampling procedure for economically measuring L_{Aeq} at mineral workings. The method is derived from a statistical analysis of noise levels measured at the East Chevington opencast coal site in Northumberland. It established that, if care is taken with the selection of the position and time of day of measurement, a standard deviation for 15-minute L_{Aeq} of 2.5dB can be achieved. For this, the measurement position should be outside the dominant influence of any one noise source from the site but within the area affected by noise from the site as a whole - such as the site boundary would normally be. In addition, the measurements must be taken when the site is working at full production, that is excluding meal breaks and tea breaks. For consistent measurements, it is also desirable for a component of wind to be blowing from the site towards the measurement point. The wind should, however, not be so strong that it generates noise at the microphone.

4.2.4.1   Application to open cast sites

The tests at East Chevington are regarded as representative of most opencast coal sites, although the 2.5 dB standard deviation found there is somewhat less than those found at other sites by the National Coal Board's "Opencast Noise Monitoring Programme" of 1982. This may be due to the NCB being less selective of their times of measurement, which are not stated explicitly in their report.

4.2.4.2 Application to other sites

The variability of noise levels at sand and gravel workings and hard rock quarries has not been evaluated, because long term noise measurements were not made at such sites. It is believed that a similar, or perhaps slightly smaller, standard deviation would apply on account of the continuously running process machinery being the main noise source as opposed to the more variable noise caused by dump trucks at opencast sites. A programme of long-term monitoring at a selection of sites could be used to confirm the values of standard deviation.

4.2.4.3 Monitoring period

The implications of a 2.5 dB standard deviation on measurement reliability are demonstrated in Figure 4.5 which shows the difference between the highest expected and the measured average L_{Aeq} related to the number of 15-minute measurements that are averaged. From this it is clear that after 1 hour of measurement the true average L_{Aeq} is likely to be no more than 2 dB above the measured average, and that a law of diminishing returns makes longer term measurements only marginally better. Therefore measurements lasting longer than 1 hour are largely unnecessary, except in situations where the measured level is so close to a limit that the potential measurement error makes it unclear whether the limit might be exceeded.

For sites where long-term limits, for example over 8 or 12 hours, are in force then short term measurements could only be used as a guide for whether exceedance was likely. A strictly valid comparison with a limit can only be made by a measurement that satisfies all the conditions of that limit.

4.2.5 Recommended noise monitoring procedure

(a) Noise monitoring should be carried out at noise control points set out in the planning consent.

41

(b)   The noise should be measured in terms of L_{Aeq} for periods of 1 hour.

(c)   Monitoring periods should be taken on a normal working day (or other periods as stipulated in the planning consent) and should avoid meal breaks.

(d)   A component of wind should be blowing from the site towards the monitoring position. Wind speed should not be so high as to generate excessive noise at the microphone.

(e)   The monitoring equipment should correspond to BS5969:1981 Type 1 (precision grade), should be calibrated before and after use, be operated in accordance with the manufacturer's instructions and in accordance with current applicable standards.

(f)   The monitoring equipment should be manned continuously to ensure that the measurements are not contaminated by extraneous noise.

(g)   Extraneous noises should be excluded by operating the "pause" button on the monitoring equipment or by equivalent means.

(h)   Where the monitored level is within 2 dB(A) of the permitted level, the measurement should be repeated on up to a further 3 occasions and the energy average of the four readings should be used for comparison with the permitted level.

(i)   This procedure should have a precision of ±1 dB(A).

4.3   Community response to noise

4.3.1 Local authority questionnaire

A questionnaire survey of local authorities was undertaken to find out which authorities were sufficiently involved with surface mineral workings to warrant a follow-up visit, and to give an indication of the importance of noise relative to other environmental effects. The questionnaire is shown in Figure 4.1. The responses were collated with reference to the predominant category of workings (opencast mine, sand and gravel pit, or hard rock quarry) in the authority's area.

Figure 4.2 shows the number of authorities registering complaints about a range of environmental effects, including visual intrusion, noise, dust, vibration, blasting and traffic. The authorities were asked to distinguish between operational sites and proposed sites. Three main causes of complaint were noted to approximately equal extents by the local authorities. These were dust, general noise, and increased traffic. Blasting and vibration, which are two manifestations of the same cause, were also a noteworthy reason for complaint at those sites where blasting occurred. Visual intrusion is perceived as a problem at the planning stage, but complaints about operational sites are low in comparison.

The relative level of complaints between proposed and operational sites shown in Figure 4.2 suggests an interesting finding, which has implications in the planning process. The noise impact anticipated by residents is somewhat worse than the reality: the opposite is true for vibration, blasting and dust, which are found to be worse than anticipated.

Traffic and visual intrusion are two other effects for which the anticipated effect is worse than reality, even though traffic is one of the worst effects of surface mineral workings.

An explanation of this finding may be that the effects of noise, traffic and visual intrusion are obvious effects readily associated with the heavy plant used in surface mineral workings - possibly through common experience with heavy road traffic - whereas other effects may not even be anticipated by residents. Furthermore, they are possibly more socially-acceptable "pegs" on which to hang less tangible fears such as loss of value of property, destruction of the countryside or a sense of fear or danger.

43

In very few cases is noise the main source of complaint (figure 4.3) although it is one of the main sources in up to 50%. Interestingly, in almost 20% of cases, it is hardly ever a source of complaint.

Although the local authority questionnaire helps to establish the relative importance of noise in the range of effects, it does not indicate the seriousness of the problem, because it does not indicate the number of complaints received by each authority, whether it be one or one hundred. Furthermore, complaint is an unreliable indicator of disturbance, as some people are habitual complainers, whilst others who may be equally concerned do not complain for a variety of reasons.

It therefore follows that noise which is acceptable to the community at large may nevertheless be a source of complaint. Furthermore, because the anticipated effect of noise at proposed sites is greater than the actual effect found at operational sites, this may add to the pressure to reduce permitted noise limits more than is strictly necessary.

4.3.2 Community studies

To obtain a further insight into the extent of the noise problem, a two-phase research study was undertaken, see Appendix D. This confirmed that surface mineral workings do not always and invariably have a major impact on local communities, and that although noise is the aspect of such workings which is most noticed in the course of daily life, dust is the greater cause of annoyance.

Noise complaints tend to be restricted to the earliest stages of a site development, particularly soil stripping and baffle mound construction. These are the stages when the operation is closest to dwellings, least well-screened and when the residents are most sensitive to the development.

When people living near surface mineral workings in Cumbria and Northumberland were interviewed, less than 20% mentioned the workings as negative features in the area. At the open cast site in South Wales, less than 16% found noise exposure levels of 43 to 48 dB(A) to be "extremely or very annoying". Given that in any social survey about 10% are very annoyed at low levels of exposure, this figure is low.

44

Reversing alarms are a dominant source of noise annoyance: over 40% of those annoyed at open cast workings cite this cause. However, there is considerable concern in some areas over road traffic, which is often linked to the site. Many people feel that noise, vibration and dust would be reduced if further traffic planning controls were implemented.

There is some evidence that good relations between the operators and the local community can increase the acceptability of surface mineral workings. The liaison committees for opencast sites were valued in this regard. Their value can be increased if the media are permitted to attend. Some residents specifically mentioned that their opinions were influenced by seeing old workings nearby, which had been restored and landscaped.

It is, perhaps, because so much concern has been expressed about noise in the past, and so much effort is now expended on the matter that it is no longer such a serious problem as anticipated. On the whole, site operators are vigilant in their attention to potential noise hazards.

Planning and Environmental Health Officers agreed that appropriate planning and site controls can cope with potential noise problems; they also acknowledged the need for widely-accepted and consistent control standards.

The very success of current noise control practice has had the parallel effect of making it very difficult, despite considerable effort, for this research to produce so-called "dose-response" relationships, for two reasons: noise levels from surface mineral workings vary greatly from week to week so that it is not possible to be certain to which noise events the residents may be responding; and secondly the noise levels experienced by residents are often so close to ambient levels that they cannot be measured reliably. The fact that these statements can be made is strong evidence that current practice in setting noise limits is generally satisfactory, but it also implies that in proposing noise limit levels, this research is restricted to unifying the best of current practice.

4.3.3 Community response - the conclusion

The general conclusion to be drawn from the surveys conducted within this project is that noise annoyance from surface mineral workings is limited in extent. However this conclusion should be interpreted cautiously. Surface mineral workings have the capability of causing annoyance, but in practice this can be limited by good planning and site management.

Bad planning, and bad management would almost certainly cause extensive noise annoyance, so it is essential that noise continues to be regarded as a very significant characteristic of surface mineral workings.

4.4   Noise limits

4.4.1 Introduction

As discussed in Section 3.6, there are two basic approaches to setting noise limit levels: either at the site boundary or at the noise sensitive-property. Both have advantages and disadvantages - boundaries are easier for access and monitoring, but do not guarantee control of noise at properties; whilst at the property, monitoring can be difficult because of low noise levels and problems of access.

These two approaches are not irreconcilable; indeed the noise limits set in recent permissions can be shown to be roughly equivalent, by means of a simplified example. The preferred approach described in this report combines the best features of both methods.

4.4.2 Reconciling limits at the boundary with limits at the dwelling

As was shown in Section 3, current practice in setting limits is apparently rather variable: for example, 57 dB(A) at the facade of dwellings, or 65 dB(A) at the site boundary are typical daytime limits. The following example demonstrates that these are broadly equivalent.

Dump trucks, the major source of noise on open-cast sites, typically produce levels of 88 to 93 dB(A) at a distance of 10m. However, as they are in constant movement along haul roads, it would be reasonable to assume that for a particular measurement point they are effectively only present at the "worst" position (where they create most noise) for, say, 50% of the time. This means that they create an equivalent noise level, L_{Aeq}, in the range of 85 to 90 dB(A). A "typical" mid-range dump truck, therefore, could give an L_{Aeq} of 87 dB(A) at a "reference distance" of 10m. To calculate the noise level at the site boundary, or at a dwelling, an allowance must be made for the attenuation (reduction) of noise over the intervening distance. This allowance can be made by using the prediction method described in section 4.1 of this report, including the absorption of noise by acoustically-soft ground. At a dwelling, the presence of the building facade causes an extra reflection of noise which adds 3 dB(A) to the level compared with a measurement in an open area (the free field) and an allowance must also be made for this where appropriate.

Taking all these factors into account, the noise level of a typical machine, generating 87 dB(A) at 10m would reduce to 65 dB(A) (free field) at 100m (see figure 4.5). Therefore, if the site boundary limit is 65 dB(A), the machine must work at an effective distance of at least 100m in order to comply with the limit.

The noise level at a dwelling depends on its distance from the site boundary and thus from the noise source. In the current example, a dwelling 150m from the boundary would be 250m from the effective source position. Taking reflections into account, its facade would be exposed to a level of 57 dB(A) L_{Aeq}, a common limit for dwellings.

Thus in the somewhat contrived but nonetheless typical circumstances of this example, a site boundary level of 65 dB(A) and a dwelling level of 57 dB(A) are equivalent. A broad equivalence will be found over a wide range of conditions.

It is obvious that the exposure of dwellings will vary according to their distance from the site boundary. For example, figure 4.6

illustrates that a level of 60 dB(A) will be reached 90m from the site boundary, and a level of 55 dB(A) will be reached 200m from the site boundary. At many sites, the nearest dwellings will be in the range 90-200m from the site boundary; therefore on many sites with a boundary limit of 65 dB(A), the exposure of dwellings could be in the range of 55-60 dB(A): this supports the view that there is a broad equivalence between the commonly-used dwelling and site boundary limits.

4.4.3 The effect of setting noise limits at the site boundary

The broad equivalence between dwelling and site boundary limits serves to indicate that the currently-used numerical values are equivalent - but the protection afforded by the two systems can differ significantly. Again, this is most easily demonstrated by an example.

In figure 4.7 a "noisy" machine producing 90 dB(A) at 10m may not work nearer than 126m to the site boundary to comply with the 65 dB(A) boundary limit. Properties nearer than 200m to the site boundary will receive over 57 dB(A): at 90m, the level will be 62 dB(A). This is 2 dB(A) more than with the typical machine, shown in figure 4.6, even though the site boundary level is the same.

Therefore, site boundary levels do not guarantee control of noise levels at dwellings and as such must be regarded as an unsatisfactory means of specifying noise limits.

4.4.4 Setting the limit at a dwelling

Suppose it is decided to set the limit to 55 dB(A) at the facade of a dwelling. It has already been shown that a dwelling 200m from the boundary will have an exposure of 55 dB(A) from a typical machine 100m inside the site. What would happen if the operator could obtain a quiet machine, giving 85 dB(A) at 10m? He could use it to within 250m of the dwelling, ie. 50m inside the site, see figure 4.8. Note, however, that this gives a site boundary level of 70 dB(A), so its use would not be permitted by a site boundary limit of 65 dB(A), which would be unnecessarily restrictive in this case.

What would happen, on the other hand, if the operator used a noisy machine giving 90 dB(A) at 10m? He would have to keep it 400m from the dwelling, ie. 200m inside the site, see figure 4.9, even though the boundary level would be only 59 dB(A). These examples further illustrate how a boundary level is unsatisfactory, both for the community and for the operator.

In the case of figure 4.8 a boundary limit would not permit the best to be obtained from a quiet machine. Figure 4.7 has shown that they do not protect dwellings from noisy machines, problems resolved by setting limits at dwellings.

4.4.5 Effect of baffle mounds

There is a final problem which is resolved by setting limits at dwellings.

Figure 4.10 shows a dwelling at 100m, where a target of 55 dB(A) is required. A typical machine would need to be 200m inside the boundary. This seems restrictive, so suppose a baffle mound is erected at the site boundary to give 10 dB(A) attenuation. It is now possible to bring the machine to within 26m of the site boundary, see figure 4.11. Note that two site boundary limits are shown - 78 dB(A) at a point exposed to the machine, and 68 dB(A) at an equivalent point in the shadow of the barrier. A boundary limit is therefore ambiguous unless it is made clear whether the monitoring point is exposed or in the shadow. Note furthermore that compared with figure 4.5, the baffle mound gives lower noise levels at a closer distance.

4.4.6 Effect of plant location on noise limits

Figure 4.6 illustrates another important aspect of surface mineral workings which needs to be considered when setting noise limits. A typical item of plant produces noise levels in the "acceptable" range of 55 to 60 dB(A) when it is 100m inside the boundary, assuming no screening. If the plant is equally likely to work in any part of the site, which is very possible over the lifetime of the site, then it can only spend about 1% of the lifetime of the site within this critical distance of the reception point. For a

20-year site, this represents a total of only 60 working days. The rest of the time, the plant must be at greater distances, causing less noise.

It is recognised that in reality, some parts of the site are more heavily used than others - major overburden dumps and semi-permanent haul roads, for example. Some sites contain static processing plant such as washers and crushers. It therefore seems desirable to recognise this variability and to set higher limits for transient working than for semi-permanent features of the site.

4.4.7 Time period of monitoring

Current monitoring periods for open cast sites usually require monitoring for a whole period, eg all day, or all night. For practical purposes, a short monitoring period is preferable, for the reasons outlined in section 3.

4.4.8 Noise limits - the proposed approach

The foregoing sections have demonstrated a broad equivalence in commonly-used noise limits and have also shown the benefit both to the operator and local community of setting limits at the sensitive properties.

Furthermore, it has been shown that if the method of working is known then it is possible to work back from the facade level to find the corresponding boundary level, by using the prediction method.

Since there are distinct advantages in monitoring at the site boundary, the preferred approach is:-

(a)   decide on the noise limit required at the noise-sensitive property appropriate for the time of day;

(b)   decide on the method of working and methods of noise control;

(c)   decide on the location of the noise control point, preferably at the site boundary;

50

(d)   use the prediction method to calculate the noise control level at the noise control point which corresponds with the dwelling noise limit;

(e)   incorporate details of the noise control levels and noise control points into the planning consent. There may be different noise control levels at each noise control point.

RESEARCH INTO THE CONTROL OF NOISE FROM SURFACE MINERAL WORKINGS
FOR THE DEPARTMENT OF THE ENVIRONMENT
BY ATKINS RESEARCH AND DEVELOPMENT

Local Authority: **Person To Contact:**

1.   Are there, or have there been, surface   Yes ☐
        mineral workings in your area?   No ☐

2.   What type(s) of operation are they?

                    Type   Approximate Number In Area

              Opencast Coal   . . . .

              Stone Quarrying   . . . .

              Chalk Quarrying   . . . .

              Gravel Extraction   . . . .

              Other (please specify)   . . . .

3.(a)   Please list the main causes of environmental complaint, if any,
        which arise from established workings.

 (b)   Please list the main causes of public concern expressed prior to
        the commencement of working.

4.   To what extent has noise been a cause of complaint?

                The main cause   ☐
                One of the main causes   ☐
                A minor but regular cause   ☐
                Hardly ever a cause   ☐

5.   Would you be interested in participating further in our research?

                        Yes   ☐
                        No   ☐

        If you are interested, please indicate the aspects of our
        research on which you would be able to provide information.

                Overall noise emission levels from sites   ☐
                Public response   ☐
                Noise levels from individual processes and   ☐
                        items of equipment
                Noise prediction methods   ☐
                Noise control methods   ☐
                Noise monitoring procedures   ☐

              FIGURE 4.1 : QUESTIONNAIRE TO LOCAL AUTHORITY

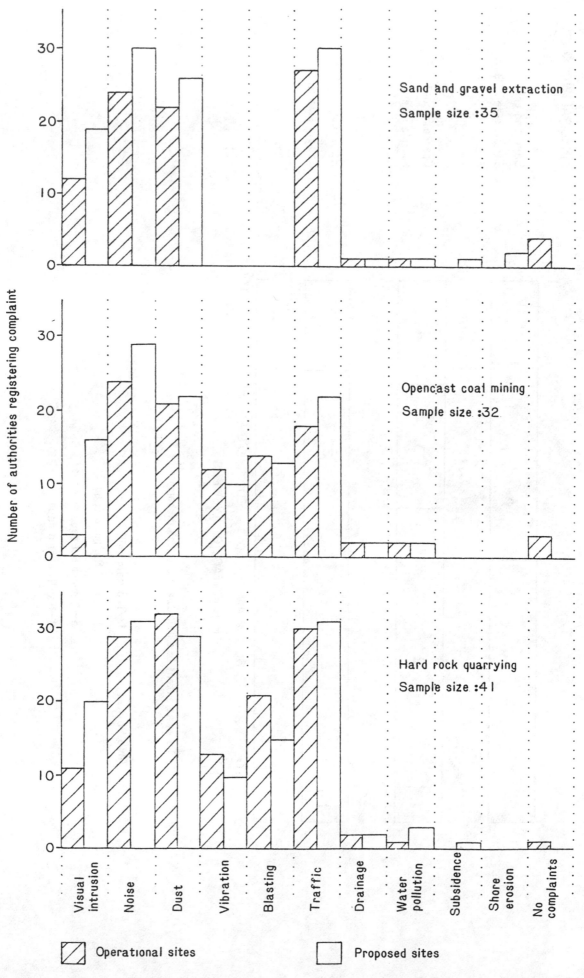

FIGURE 4.2 : ANALYSIS OF ENVIRONMENTAL EFFECTS

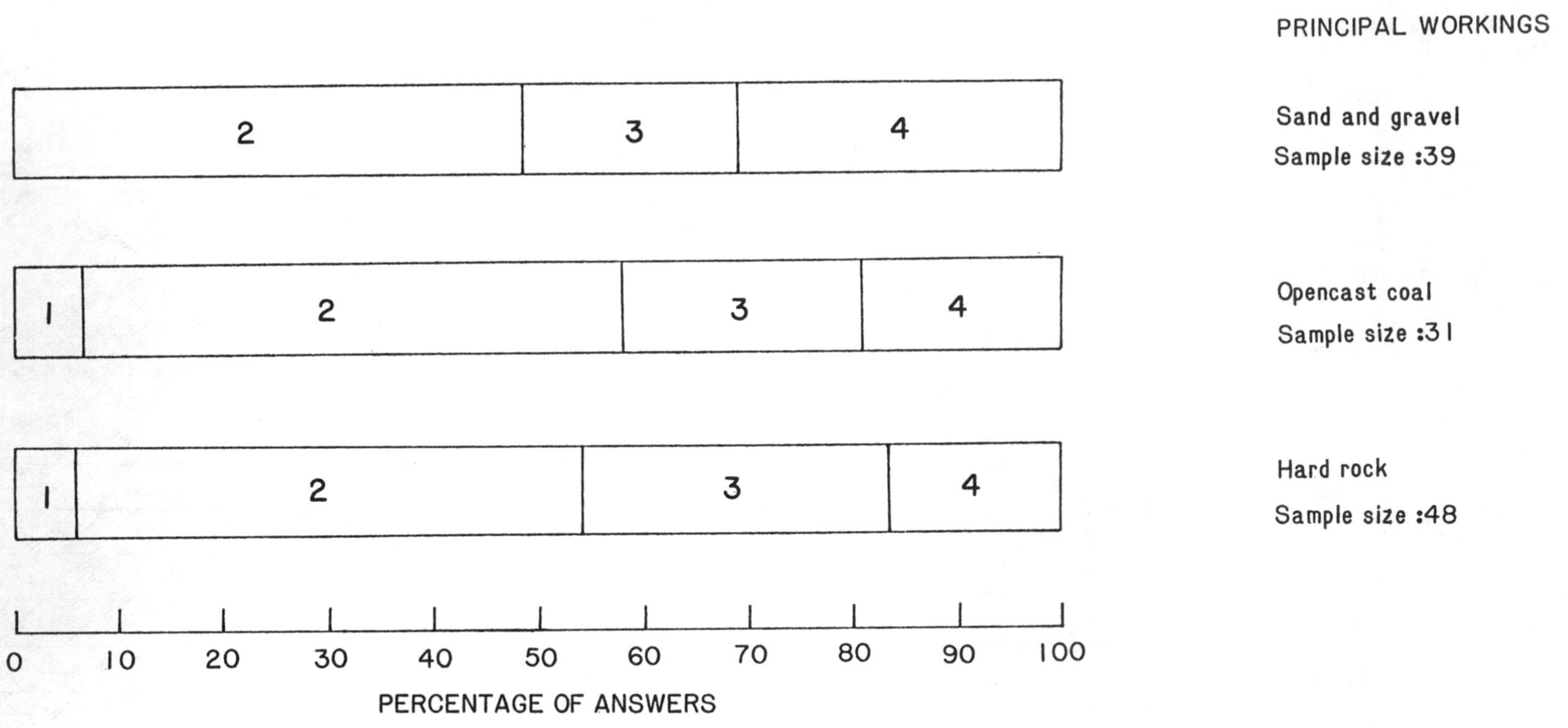
PRINCIPAL WORKINGS
Sand and gravel
Sample size :39
Opencast coal
Sample size :31
Hard rock
Sample size :48
0
10
20
30
40
50
60
70
80
90
100
PERCENTAGE OF ANSWERS

QUESTION : To what extent has noise been a cause of complaint

POSSIBLE ANSWERS :

1—The main cause
2—One of the main causes
3—A minor but regular cause
4—Hardly ever a cause

FIGURE 4.3 : IMPORTANCE OF NOISE AS A NUISANCE

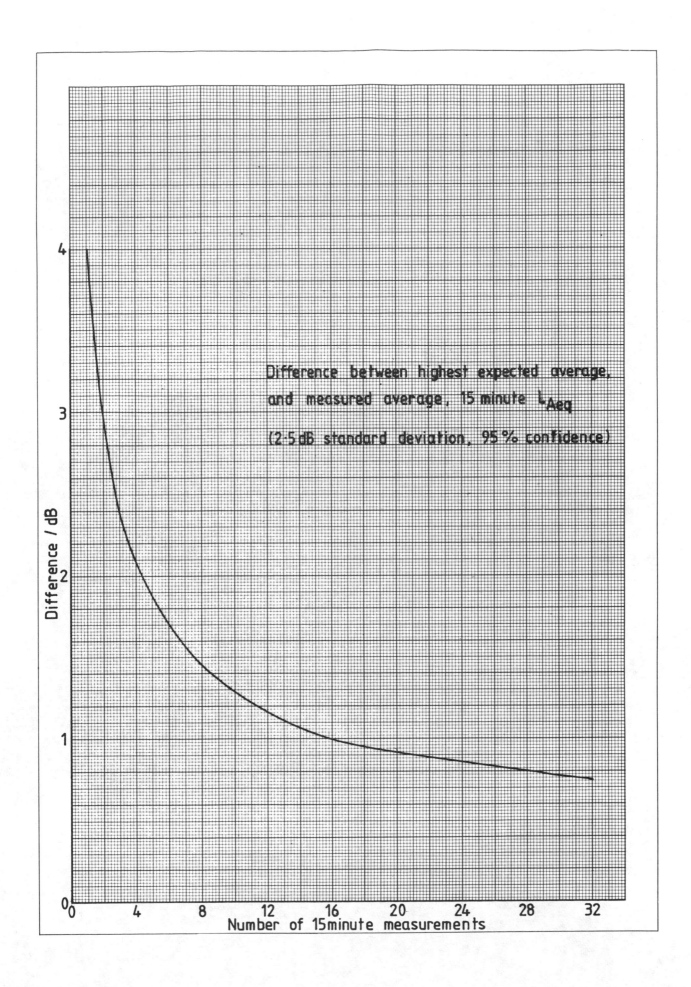

FIGURE 4.4 : NOISE MEASUREMENT ACCURACY

EFFECT OF
65dB(A) NOISE LIMIT AT SITE BOUNDARY

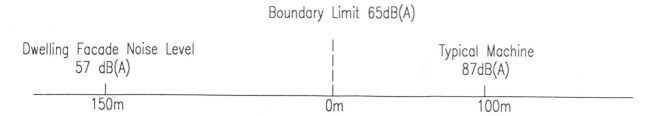

Boundary Limit 65dB(A)

Dwelling Facade Noise Level
57 dB(A)

Typical Machine
87dB(A)

150m   0m   100m

Figure 4.5 Boundary and Dwelling Noise Levels for a Typical Machine

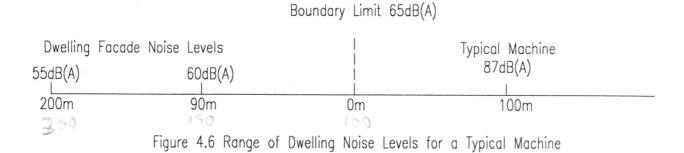

Boundary Limit 65dB(A)

Dwelling Facade Noise Levels

55dB(A)   60dB(A)

Typical Machine
87dB(A)

200m   90m   0m   100m

Figure 4.6 Range of Dwelling Noise Levels for a Typical Machine

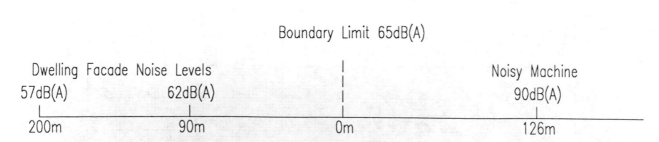

Boundary Limit 65dB(A)

Dwelling Facade Noise Levels

57dB(A)   62dB(A)

Noisy Machine
90dB(A)

200m   90m   0m   126m

Figure 4.7 Range of Dwelling Noise Levels for a Noisy Machine

EFFECT OF
55dB(A) NOISE LIMIT AT DWELLING FACADE

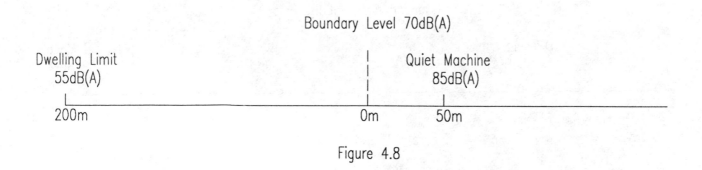

Figure 4.8

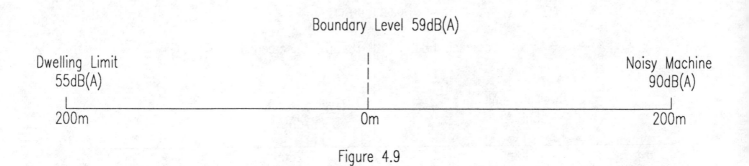

Figure 4.9

EFFECT OF BAFFLE MOUND

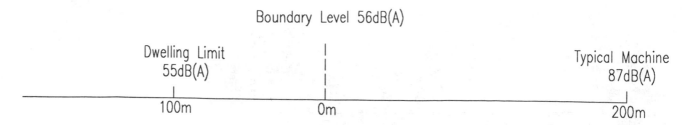

Boundary Level 56dB(A)

Dwelling Limit
55dB(A)

Typical Machine
87dB(A)

100m   0m   200m

Figure 4.10 No Baffle Mound

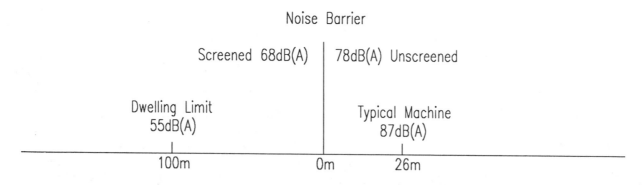

Noise Barrier

Screened 68dB(A) | 78dB(A) Unscreened

Dwelling Limit
55dB(A)

Typical Machine
87dB(A)

100m   0m   26m

Figure 4.11 With Baffle Mound Giving 10dB(A)

5.0 IMPLICATIONS FOR FUTURE PRACTICE

5.1 Planning controls

5.1.1 Considerations in setting noise limits

Planning conditions should contain limits on the noise emission from surface mineral workings to ensure adequate safeguards for noise sensitive properties. However, it is frequently impracticable to monitor for compliance with noise limits at the noise-sensitive property itself, firstly because there may be problems of access, and secondly because there may be extraneous noise arising from roads, other sources and even the property itself.

Fortunately, in the case of surface mineral workings, it is possible to establish noise control points (ie. noise monitoring locations) at a distance from the noise-sensitive property and to calculate noise control levels which correspond to the noise limit required at the property.

The noise control points can be in locations accessible to the site operator and the mineral planning authority, sufficiently free of extraneous noise and suitably positioned relative to the noise sources affecting the noise-sensitive properties. The site boundary will generally be the preferred location for a noise control point.

Where the noise control point is at the site boundary, the noise control level will be higher than the noise limit required at the property, to take account of the decay of noise level over the intervening distance. The precise value will be calculated in accordance with the noise prediction technique described below.

The noise monitoring period should be short enough to permit measurements to be attended, to ensure that the results are not affected by extraneous noise or by abnormal operating conditions or weather.

Currently commonly-applied noise limits appear to give satisfactory safeguards at opencast sites. These are in the form of fixed equivalent continuous (L_{eq}) values applicable to different times of the day and week. (The arguments against limits relative to existing levels are given in Section 3.6.3). There is no reason to believe that these will not be equally satisfactory for other types of surface mineral workings, provided due allowance is made for the more continuous noise which may arise from fixed plant and facilities including haul roads.

5.1.2 Recommended noise limits

Accordingly, our recommendations on noise limits are as follows:

Noise limits should be set in units of L_{Aeq} (1 hour) 1m in front of the most exposed of any windows and doors in the facade of a noise-sensitive property. Areas of open space to which the public have access for quiet relaxation can be considered for these purposes to be noise-sensitive, provided they are of importance in planning terms. Isolated footpaths, for example, would not be recognised as noise-sensitive.

During the working week the daytime limit (typically 0700-1900 hours) should be in the range of 55 to 60 dB L_{Aeq} (1 hour).

More stringent limits within the range 50 to 55 dB L_{Aeq} daytime may be imposed for fixed plant and facilities in continuous use, including haul roads, as described in Section 4.4.5. 4.4.6

During the working week the night time limit (typically 2200-0600 hours) should be in the range of 40 to 45 dB L_{Aeq} (1 hour).

Where a different limit is considered appropriate for an evening or early morning period this should be in the range 45 to 50 dB L_{Aeq} (1 hour).

A different time schedule of the above limits can be applied at weekend.

Compliance with the above limits is to be monitored as described in Section 5.2 below.

The above limits may be suspended for the construction and removal of baffle mounds and other work of a temporary nature for which it can be demonstrated that it would not be reasonably practicable to meet the limit.

5.2 Noise monitoring

Monitoring noise emissions for compliance with planning conditions should be undertaken at the established noise control points using a suitable sampling procedure, as described below. Where a nuisance is alleged, it may also be appropriate to monitor at the complainant's property.

The noise should be measured in terms of L_{Aeq} for periods of 1 hour.

Monitoring periods should be taken on a normal working day (or other periods as stipulated in the planning consent) and should avoid meal breaks.

A component of wind should be blowing from the site towards the monitoring position. Wind speed should not be so high as to generate excessive noise at the microphone.

The monitoring equipment should correspond to Type 1 (precision) grade, should be calibrated before and after use, be operated in accordance with the manufacturer's instructions and in accordance with current applicable standards.

The monitoring equipment should be manned continuously to ensure that the measurements are not contaminated by extraneous noise.

Extraneous noise should be excluded by operating the "pause" button on the monitoring equipment or by equivalent means.

Where the monitored level is within 2 dB(A) of the permitted level, the measurement should be repeated on up to a further three occasions and the energy average of the four readings should be used for comparison with the permitted level.

This procedure should have a precision of ± 1 dB(A).

5.3   Noise prediction

MPA and operators should be encouraged to use a commonly agreed prediction technique.

Of the currently available techniques, BS5228 provides the most appropriate basic approach and gives good prediction accuracy provided:

(a)   the sound power levels used in calculations apply to the actual plant in use on the site; and

(b)   the correction shown in Appendix B is applied to haul roads which subtend less than 180 degrees "angle of view" at the calculation point.

The prediction accuracy can be further improved by making the alternative correction shown in Appendix B for soft ground attenuation when this is greater than the barrier correction.

5.4   Abatement measures

5.4.1 Baffle mounds and acoustic enclosures

Baffle mounds at the perimeter of a site can significantly reduce the exposure of noise-sensitive properties. The agreed prediction technique must be sensitive to the contribution that they can make to the reduction of noise.

The process of constructing baffle mounds itself constitutes an additional noise impact and operators should consider temporary screening to limit that impact when reasonably practicable and where there is a particularly sensitive local need.

It may be appropriate for MPAs and operators to reach an agreement that, for a specified (and short) period, the noise limits applicable to specific monitoring points, be suspended.

Fencing can provide protection where insufficient land is available for a baffle mound, or where a baffle mound would prevent the extraction of a significant mineral resource. The use of fencing on top of a baffle mound can provide increased protection, or reduce the land take required for a given degree of protection. The differences in impact on the landscape must also be considered.

The provision of appropriate acoustic enclosures should be considered, particularly for fixed plant and equipment, and should be a requirement where necessary for noise limits to be met.

Straw bales can provide effective temporary screening to localised noise sources close to the ground.

5.4.2 Separation distances

Previously, it has been suggested that there should be a minimum separation distance between workings and the nearest noise-sensitive property.

However, there is now a reliable prediction technique to permit the noise effects of proposed operations to be calculated and compared with noise limits.

The noise limits will determine the separation distances required for any particular method of working, and the separation distance can be reliably calculated by means of the proposed prediction method. There is therefore no reason for a separation distance to be stipulated as an independent means of noise control.

There may be non-acoustic reasons for limiting the proximity of workings to the site boundary. For example, the stability of adjacent land, and the quality of residential visual amenity are material matters for consideration, but these are not acoustic matters.

5.4.3 Work sequencing and site layout

The sequence and direction of working and the site layout should be agreed between MPAs and operators before the commencement of working. Such agreement must allow flexibility of working within acceptable parameters and must recognise that noise control is not the only environmental or operational parameter to be considered in determining the sequence and direction of working.

The workings should wherever possible be arranged so that earlier operations provide screening for noise-sensitive properties from the noise generated by subsequent operations.

In particular, if excavation proceeds towards the noise-sensitive properties, the excavation face can provide considerable protection to those properties.

Fixed plant and facilities, including maintenance areas and permanent haul roads, should be so located as to minimise their impact on noise-sensitive properties.

5.4.4 Equipment selection

It is not considered to be the role of MPAs to select the particular make or model of equipment to be used on a particular site, as they would not have the requisite operational experience, financial responsibility or information on performance of the equipment.

Insofar as the plant selection affects the work sequencing and site layout, for example the choice between conveyor belt and dump truck for transporting materials, this will be discussed between MPA and applicant as set out in 5.4.3 above.

However, MPAs will wish to verify any submissions made by the applicant regarding noise impact, and for that purpose may require that applicant to supply data on the sound power level generated by the proposed equipment.

Such data, if determined by a competent acoustic agency, can be used in place of the information contained in BS5228 Part 1 Appendix C for prediction purposes.

Under EC Regulations, many items of plant are now required to be noise certificated by a NAMAS accredited agency. Such an agency would be a "competent acoustic agency". Alternatively, any agency which could demonstrate compliance with the relevant British Standards would be so qualified.

5.4.5 Maintenance

In addition to the noise limits in Section 5.1 above, MPAs may also wish to constrain the hours during which maintenance work can be conducted outside a suitably insulated maintenance building.

It is impracticable to require maintenance schedules to be agreed as part of planning conditions, but operators should be encouraged to undertake a programme of preventative maintenance of plant and equipment.

Of particular significance to the generation of noise is attention to:

- the integrity of silencers
- the lubrication of bearings
- the sharpness of cutting edges

5.5 Public relations

It is important both for operators and MPAs that active steps be taken for the fostering of good relations between the operator and the local community, by establishing good communications.

The potential operator of a site may be required to submit proposals to the MPA for the encouragement of good communications with the local community.

For larger workings the establishment of a liaison committee may well be appropriate. This is increasingly common in the context of opencast coal sites.

It has been found that where local residents have seen workings that have been reclaimed and landscaped, they are more willing to tolerate a temporary loss of amenity.

5.6 Best practicable means

It is unnecessary and inappropriate to impose a planning condition required by "best practicable means" of noise control to be adopted at surface mineral workings.

It is unnecessary because satisfactory noise control can be obtained by the use of noise limits as set out in Section 5 of this report.

It is inappropriate firstly because "best practicable means" may be legally void as a planning condition through uncertaintly as to what constitutes such means. Secondly, it does not address the question of whether the workings will be environmentally acceptable and gives no indication of the effect which the workings will have on noise-sensitive property.

5.7 Vehicle reversing alarms

A major component in annoyance caused by noise from surface mineral works is the sound of reversing alarms which are legally required under the Quarries Vehicles Regulations. Such alarms can cause annoyance at considerable distances from a site, even though the background noise level is higher than that caused by the alarms.

Operators should be encouraged to use directional alarms and to ensure as far as possible that vehicles reverse away from noise-sensitive properties.

Although there are alternatives, they are currently neither wholly reliable nor suitable for all types of vehicles. Research into the matter is continuing.

5.8 Offsite road traffic

Offsite road traffic can cause a number of problems, including noise, and MPAs should consider its effect.

It is suggested that one form of assessment is to calculate the increment in noise level above that currently prevailing, as predicted by 'Calculation of Road Traffic Noise 1988'.

The current research has not set out to consider what increment might be acceptable, but it is generally accepted that changes of less than 3 dB(A) are not significant.

APPENDIX A

REVIEW OF PUBLISHED LITERATURE

A.1 Legislation and Official Reports

The extraction of minerals, whilst bringing undoubted benefits to the nation's standard of living and its economy, is often controversial. Minerals can only be worked where they lie in the ground, which can well be in environmentally sensitive areas. Minerals planning has to balance the needs of society for minerals with the protection of the environment, and ensure that any adverse environmental impact is kept to an acceptable level.

The Town and Country Planning Act 1971 as amended by the Minerals Act 1981 provides the main legislative framework for minerals planning, following from the Stevens Report (1975) which had examined the statutory provisions for mineral working. The Act requires far more stringent aftercare conditions on site operators than had previously applied, and imposes on the mineral planning authorities a requirement to carry out periodical reviews of all mineral sites in their area with a view to maintaining their standards of environmental acceptability. By this means it is possible to impose up-to-date environmental standards on old as well as new workings.

Minerals planning is the responsibility of the County Councils, London Boroughs, Metropolitan Districts and National Park Planning Boards. These authorities are required to guide future development and land use in their respective areas, and to allow or refuse development proposals submitted to them. The system is not intended to impose an unreasonable degree of regulation. DoE Circular 14/85 "Development and Employment" emphasises the presumption in favour of allowing applications for development unless demonstrable harm would be made to interests of acknowledged importance.

The specific case of opencast coal mining was brought under the control of the mineral planning authorities by the provisions of the Housing and Planning Act 1986, following from the statement of intent in the 1983 White Paper "Coal and the Environment", which itself followed from the 1981 Flowers Commission Report.

The May 1988 Minerals Planning Guidance Notes MPG3, give guidance to the mineral planning authorities for deciding applications to mine opencast coal. MPG3 recommends the use of environmental impact assessments by the developer to support an application for planning permission, and refers to BS5228 for guidance to authorities on noise. Further guidance relating to noise appears in DoE Circular 1/85 on "The Use of Conditions in Planning Permissions", where the need for precise and enforceable planning conditions is emphasised.

The Control of Pollution Act 1974 is important legislation for noise control, but is not applied to surface mineral workings. However, it introduces a number of important principles. It requires a local authority to inspect its area periodically for noise nuisances and empowers the authority to serve a notice under section 58 of the Act requiring the abatement of a nuisance. Section 59 allows an individual person to prosecute for noise nuisance in the magistrates court. The Act develops the possibility of a defending a noise nuisance case on the ground that the "best practicable means" have been used to limit the noise nuisance. In its guidelines defining "best practicable means", the Act requires reference to approved codes of practice of which, in the case of surface mineral workings, BS5228 is an example. DoE Circular 2/76 "Control of Pollution Act 1974 - Implementation of Part III - Noise" expands on the requirements of the Act, and emphasises the desirability of co-operation between the local authority and those responsible for producing noise in order that there should be a mutually co-operative approach to reducing noise. It describes various methods of noise control which might reasonably be considered to reduce noise emissions.

The earlier DoE Circular 10/73 "Planning and Noise" had given broad guidelines for considering noise. It advises planning authorities to seek to avoid the creation of situations where industry might inflict noise on neighbouring noise sensitive property although it recognises that in some cases, for example mineral workings, it may be necessary to allow such situations to meet other planning objectives. For assessing proposed development in general it advocates the use of BS4142.

The report of the Wilson Committee (1963), although fairly old, maintains its value as an exhaustive survey of the generation and effects of noise from many types of source in many environments. Its section on surface mineral workings likens some aspects of the work, such as the moving of topsoil and overburden, to civil engineering. On the other hand, aspects such as fixed or semi-permanent processing plant are likened to industrial activities for the purposes of noise control. It notes few complaints of noise or blasting at mineral workings, and reports the use of limited working hours, care in the siting of processing plant and the fitting of efficient silencers as methods for reducing noise. The report recommends that noise assessment should be on the same basis as for construction sites or industrial premises, whichever is more appropriate to the operations on the site.

It is rare to find noise limits stated in any legislation or official reports. The Flowers Commission report (1981) on "Coal and the Environment" is an exception to this. It identifies the stripping and re-spreading of topsoil, and the noise caused by dump trucks, as the main sources of noise nuisance on an opencast coal site. It goes on to recommended maximum noise levels of 65dB(A) L_{Aeq} by day and 55 dB(A) L_{Aeq} by night to be allowed for coaling operations, with these limits needing to be relaxed for topsoil stripping. The particular case of Butterwell in Northumberland, with its limits of 57dB(A) L_{Aeq} by day and 50dB(A) L_{Aeq} by night is also mentioned in this report.

A.2 British Standards

The British Standard most relevant to surface mineral workings noise is BS5228 (1984) "Noise control on construction and open sites". The Standard gives guidance applicable to all types of construction and open site in its Part 1, and guidance specific to opencast coal sites in Part 3.

Part 1 includes recommended methods of assessing neighbourhood noise nuisance. It advises the use of L_{Aeq} for describing long-term site noise, and presents a fairly straightforward method of estimating the likely neighbourhood noise levels caused by a site. This method is one of those evaluated in Section 4.1 of this report.

The Standard recognises that it is difficult to give detailed guidance on criteria for setting noise control targets, but suggests the factors which should be considered. These are: the site location relative to noise-sensitive premises, the existing ambient noise levels, the duration of noisy site operations, the times of day and days of the week when work is carried out, the amount of goodwill between the site operator and the local public, and the characteristics of the site's noise (for example the presence of impulses or pure tones).

In its suggestions for controlling noise, the standard recommends the reduction of noise at its source by the use of inherently quieter models of plant, by acoustic treatment of machinery in consultation with the manufacturer, by the erection of acoustic enclosures, and by regular equipment maintenance. The importance of good planning and supervision is emphasised, to achieve the optimum layout of the site and to ensure adherence to working methods and noise levels. The benefits to be gained from using barriers as noise screens are also discussed.

An appendix to Part 1 of the Standard gives typical sound power levels for most of the common types of equipment found at surface mineral workings. Although a useful guide, this data does not refer to specific makes and models of equipment and does not allow for variations in the noise levels between different operating

71

conditions, so it is not a good substitute for measurements of actual items of equipment in their common modes of operation. Part 3 of the Standard applies the principles contained in Part 1 to consider the specific example of opencast coal workings.

Another British Standard commonly associated with surface mineral workings is BS4142 (1967). Its general use is widespread in the UK for rating noise nuisance. Although its original intended application was to "factories, industrial premises and other fixed installations affecting residential areas", it has been used for wider applications in the absence of other more specific rating methods. Its application to surface mineral workings is rather controversial since the nature of the noise from such workings is somewhat different to industrial noise, but in the absence of an alternative method its use is favoured by some local authorities. There are others, such as British Coal, who positively discourage its use.

The method uses an A-weighted sound pressure level (as the Standard predates L_{Aeq}) suitably corrected for duration, tonal components and impulsive characteristics. The corrected level, determined outside a noise sensitive property, is compared to the background level (for example L_{90}). If the corrected level is higher by 10dB(A) or more then complaints are considered likely, and a difference of 5dB(A) is deemed to be of marginal significance.

A.3. Technical Papers

Very few technical papers have been written on the subject of noise from the various types of surface mineral workings, reflecting the general lack of detailed knowledge on the subject. The majority of these are concerned with particular items of equipment although there have also been some general reviews of noise from surface mineral workings, especially opencast coal.

The paper by Utley (1980) on "Noise from Opencast Coal Mining Sites" describes the principal sources of noise from opencast mining, highlighting the soil stripping and baffle mound construction in the early stages of a site's life as being the noisiest operations. The dump trucks are said to be the main source of noise once the site has become established.

Utley discusses the problems of assessing the nuisance caused by opencast coal mining noise in the absence of any directly relevant detailed information. He suggests that a suitable noise index might be L_{Aeq}, but hesitates to apply commonly quoted "acceptable" noise levels in a situation where public attitudes could be highly significant. It is pointed out that attitudes could be influenced by other environmental factors such as visual intrusion.

He comments on the importance of being able to reliably predict noise levels, mentions some of the possible methods, and discusses shortfalls of the methods such as not allowing for meteorological conditions, and predicting attenuation over long distances. Methods of noise control such as barrier mounds, acoustic treatment of earthmoving machinery, and noise insulation of affected properties are described. It is concluded that there is insufficient information available to enable a scheme for the control of noise from opencast sites to be produced.

The paper by Walton (1981) describes the opencast operation, and reports measurements of various site operations at Oughterside in Cumbria including at nearby residential properties. Noise control measures are said to have developed through "expendiency and

73

compromise", and the paper calls for a socio-acoustic study to resolve the difficulties associated with planning and monitoring sites to restrict noise nuisance.

Tomlinson (1985) discusses many of the aspects of opencast mining affecting the environment. In his comments on noise, he cites a normal L_{Aeq} limit as 65dB(A) for the 12 hour period from 0700 hours to 1900 hours on weekdays (0700 to 1300 on Saturdays) and 55dB(A) for the night-time from 1900 to 0700 hours, at the site boundary. Examples of variations on this are given - 57dB(A) from 0600 to 2200, 57dB(A) over any shift, 70dB(A) from 0700 to 1900, and 67dB(A) from 0700 to 1900. He describes techniques used for measuring the ambient noise levels as part of the pre-site planning, for monitoring site boundary noise levels, and for checking the noise of individual items of plant.

Other technical papers concentrate on noise reduction methods for particular items of equipment. Work on front-end loaders by Dixon and Bartholamae (1982) was carried out for the US Bureau of Mines, and concentrated on two models : a Caterpillar 988 and on International H-400B. The intention was to reduce noise in the operator's cab rather than to reduce the general emission of noise, so most of the methods adopted would not be applicable to the present study. The main sources of noise were identified as the engine and fan (despite factory installed exhaust silencers), with the transmission and hydraulics contributing to a lesser extent.

Bucket-wheel excavators have been studied in a manner more relevant to this present study, by Roddewig (1984) for the manufacturers M.A.N. Nurnberg. The main noise sources were found to be the bucket-wheel drive and the conveyor drives. Minor sources were the conveyor lines and noise caused by resonances in the excavator's structure. The total sound power level before acoustic treatment was found to be 125dB(A). Large surface- absorption type baffles were fitted over the main noise sources with due regard to heat dissipation, access for maintenance, and safety. The resulting sound power level was 116dB(A), a reduction of 9 dB(A).

Giardino and Marraccini (1979) give noise levels for equipment used in treatment plants, both for coal and other minerals. A major source is identified as the shakeout device which vibrates a railway hopper in order to discharge the coal or ore through the hopper doors on the underside of the vehicle. At the operator's position, the sound pressure level is given as between 118 and 122dB(A). Other sources are crushers (100 to 107dB(A)) which reduce the size of large blocks of mineral, and vibrating screens (100 to 105dB(A)) which sort the mineral by size. Slide chutes used for transporting the mineral around the plant are said to produce 95 to 100 dB(A).

A.4   List of references

BS4142 (1967) (as amended)
"Method of rating industrial noise affecting mixed residential and industrial areas".

BS5228 (1984)
"Noise control on construction and open sites"

BS5969 (1981)
"Specification for sound level meters"

Broadhurst, K A, and Wilton, T J (1983)
"Opencast Mining and Quarrying and other activities using explosives - an assessment of human and physical impact", Proceedings Inter-Noise 1983, pp. 969-972.

Browning, H J (1979)
"Mobile Equipment Noise Control in Surface Mining", Proc. Inter-Noise 1983, pp 283-289.

Calculation of Road Traffic Noise (1988)
HMSO

Coal and the Environment (1983)
The Government's response to the Flowers Commission on Energy and the Environment's Report on 'Coal and the Environment', Cmnd. 8877

CONCAWE Report No. 4/81
The propogation of Noise from Petroleum and Petrochemical Complexes to Neighbouring Communities

Control of Pollution Act 1974
HMSO

DoE Circular 10/73
"Planning and Noise", HMSO (1973)

DoE Circular 2/76
"Control of Pollution Act 1974 - Implementation of Part III Noise", HMSO (1976).

DoE Circular 3/84
"Opencast Coal Mining", HMSO (1984)

DoE Circular 1/85
The use of Conditions in Planning Permissions", HMSO (1985)

Diggory, I.S. and Oakes, B (1980)
"Butterwell Opencast Coal Site Noise Project Final Report",
Newcastle upon Tyne Polytechnic, July 1980.

Dixon, N R and Bartholomae, R S (1982)
"Front-end loader noise control", Proc Inter-noise 1982, pp 277-280.

EEC draft directive 4590/86
"Limitation of noise emitted by hydraulic excavators, rope-operated
excavators, dozers, loaders and excavator-loaders", report of EEC
Permanent Representatives Committee, January 1986.

Flowers Commission (1981)
"Coal and the Environment", HMSO

Giardino, D A and Marraccini, LC (1979)
"Noise in the Mining Industry - an overview", Proc. Inter-noise
1979, pp 263-273

Health and Safety at Work, etc Act 1974
HMSO

Holmes, A T and van Niekerk, F (1982)
"The Solution of a Community Noise Problem Caused Inter Alia by Duct
Extraction Fans on Surface Plants", J Mine Vent. Soc of South
Africa, December 1982 pp 116-120.

Housing and Planning Act 1986
HMSO

ISO 1996 (1982)
"Acoustics - Description and Measurement of Environmental Noise".

ISO 6393 (1985)
"Acoustics - Measurement of airborne noise emitted by earthmoving machinery - Method for determining compliance with limits for exterior noise - Stationary test condition"

ISO/DIS 6395 (1986)
"Acoustics - Measurement of airbourne noise emitted by earthmoving machinery - Method for determining compliance with limits for exterior noise - Simulated work cycle test conditions".

Mabey, R. (1987)
"Minerals Planning - The General Approach", Mine & Quarry, Feb 1987

Minerals Planning Guidance MPG3 (1988)
"Opencast Coal Mining", HMSO

Noise Advisory Council (1975)
"Noise Units", HMSO

Noise Advisory Council (1978)
"A Guide to Measurement and Prediction of the Equivalent Continuous Sound Level Leq", HMSO

Oil Companies Materials Association (1972)
Procedural Specification for Limitation of Noise and Equipment for use in the Petroleum Industry, Specification no. NWG 1

Quarry Vehicle Regulations 1970
HMSO

Robinson, D W (1972)
"An essay in comparison of environmental noise measures and prospects for a unified system", NPL Acoustics Report Ac 59.

Robinson, D W (1977)
"Practice and principle in environmental noise rating", NPL Acoustics report Ac 81.

Rodderig, H (1984)

"Noise analysis and emission control for a large bucket-wheel excavator (BWE)", Res. Eng. Manuf., n. 15, 1984

Shultz, T J (1982)

"Community Noise Rating", Applied Science Publishers.

Staiano, M A (1982)

"Environmental noise from Surface Mining Operations", Proc. Inter Noise 1982, pp 285-288.

Stevens Report (1975)

"Planning Control and Mineral Working", HMSO

Tomlinson J D (1985)

"Opencast Mining and the Environment", Colliery Guardian, June 1985.

Town and Country Planning (Minerals) Act 1981
HMSO

Utley, W A (1980)

"Noise from opencast coal sites", Applied Acoustics 13 (1980), pp 85-102

Wakefield Metropolitan District Council (1978)

"An investigation into certain environmental problems - Pugney's open-cast coal site", Report by Environmental Health Department.

Walton, W P (1981)

"Noise emissions from opencast coal extraction sites", Noise and Vibration Control Worldwide, Dec 1981.

Wilson Committee (1963)

"Noise-Final Report", HMSO, Cmnd 2056.

Willson, T K

"Noise and the extraction, treatment and distribution of Minerals", Minerals and the Environment, Vol 3, pp 31-46.

APPENDIX B

NOISE PREDICTION STUDIES

B.1   Method of study

Studies of noise prediction methods were carried out to determine those methods which were most applicable to surface mineral workings. This was achieved by comparing noise levels predicted by each of the methods with actual measured levels, at eighteen positions covering four surface mineral workings. The workings comprised two opencast coal sites, a sand and gravel pit, and a limestone quarry. The measurement fieldwork is described in Appendix C.

Sections B.2 and B.3 of this appendix describe the various modifications that were applied to the basic prediction methods of BS5228 and Concawe. Reference should be made to the original publications for full descriptions of the basic methods. The results of the modifications are summarised in Tables B1 and B2 which show the least squares correlation coefficient, slope and intercept for all of the comparisons of predicted and measured levels, for each modification to the prediction method. An ideal prediction method would combine a very low mean error with a correlation coefficient of r = 1.0 with a slope of 1 and an intercept of 0.

B.2   BS5228

The BS5228 method was tested in its basic form, and with the modifications described below. Figure B5 shows graphs of predicted level plotted against measured level for each modification. The dashed reference line in each graph is predicted level = measured level, the ideal result.

B.2.1 Soft Ground Attenuation

BS5228 contains a correction for geometrical spreading (attenuation over distance) but no allowance is made for the effect of ground

80

attenuation. As surface mineral workings tend to be in rural locations, the extra attenuation over soft ground could have a considerable effect on the resulting noise level.

The scope of this study was not such that a detailed investigation could be made into attenuation rates over soft ground which can involve complex frequency-dependent interference effects. However, soft ground corrections from two other prediction methods (CONCAWE and CRTN) were tested as an addition to the basic BS5228 method. It is generally accepted that barriers intercept the ground ray that is responsible for the interference effects observed over soft ground. Consequently, soft ground effects and barrier attenuation are not additive. Thus, in these tests an additional allowance was made for either barrier attenuation or soft ground attenuation, whichever was the greater, when calculating the contribution from each source. The values used in making this additional allowance are shown graphically in Figure B1.

The CONCAWE soft ground attenuation is given for octave band frequencies from 63 Hz up to 4 kHz. This was converted into a correction which could be subtracted from the A-weighted source sound power level by logarithmically averaging the ground attenuation for the most significant 3 octave bands, 500, 1k and 2k Hz.

This soft ground correction took no account of the average height of propagation above ground from the source to the receiver position. For cases where the average height of propagation above ground is high, the correction used would be too high and so the predicted noise level should be lower than measured.

The other soft ground correction considered was taken from the "Calculation of Road Traffic Noise". This is a correction which can be subtracted from the A-weighted noise level. Unlike the CONCAWE correction, the average height of propagation above ground is taken into consideration, but nevertheless resulted in under-prediction of noise levels. This may be a result of extrapolating the CRTN curves well beyond their stated limit of accuracy, which is 300m. The CRTN curves show increasing attenuation with distance, whereas the CONCAWE curves approach a limit at 400m, of 6 dB(A).

B.2.2 Varying Barrier Attenuation

The correction for barrier attenuation used in BS5228 is as follows: if a noise source is just visible from the receiver, the correction is 5dB; if the noise source is completely screened, the correction is 10dB. Apart from the interpretation of "just visible" this seems a reasonable approximation to make if very little is known about topographical features in the area or detailed heights of barriers. However BS5228 does comment that "...high topographical features and specifically designed and positioned noise barriers could provide significantly greater attenuation".

As the topographical and barrier information was available for the four sites considered, it was decided to investigate barrier attenuation which varied with the difference in path length due to the presence of the barrier.

For barrier attenuation CONCAWE uses the Maekawa curve, which is well established for accurately calculating the barrier attenuation of point sources of known frequency. Using a similar method to that used for calculating the soft ground absorption, the correction for the most significant frequencies was logarithmically averaged to give a correction which could be used with the A-weighted noise level.

The Calculation of Road Traffic Noise uses a curve similar to the Maekawa curve, but the correction is already in a form which can be used as the correction to an A-weighted level. This was therefore tested as an alternative to the CONCAWE form. The two approaches are illustrated graphically in Figure B2.

B.2.3 Soft Ground Attenuation and Barrier Attenuation

Each combination of the soft ground attenuation and varying barrier attenuation outlined in the previous sections was tested. Either soft ground attenuation or barrier attenuation was used but not both. The most effective, ie the higher, of the two corrections was used for each source.

B.2.4 Treatment of Mobile Plant on Site

This final modification to BS5228 was of a slightly different nature to the other modifications investigated. The method of treating a specific type of source was altered, rather than a correction added or modified. The source considered was "mobile plant on site" meaning a moving source, but one which only moves over a restricted area.

BS5228 treats mobile plant on site in the following manner: the minimum distance, which is not necessarily the perpendicular distance, between the source path and the receiver is found and the distance correction applied as for a stationary source. An equivalent percentage on-time is calculated from the ratio of traverse length to minimum distance, where the traverse length is the distance travelled on site by the plant. This is multiplied by the actual percentage on-time to give a corrected on-time. The mobile plant on site is then treated as if it were stationary at the minimum distance from the receiver, but given an equivalent percentage on-time to correct for the time the plant is further away from the receiver.

This treatment gives rise to some problems. Firstly, if the path of the plant is screened for part of its length the method gives no indication of how to calculate the effective attenuation. Also, two similar situations could give the same predicted noise level where this is clearly not the case. Figure B3 shows two situations with the same minimum distance and the same traverse length and hence the same equivalent percentage on-time. However situation (a) should give a higher noise level than situation (b).

The alteration tested in this study was to treat the mobile plant on site in a similar way to vehicles on haul roads, as a line source rather than as a point source. The distance correction was calculated as shown in Figure B4 using the minimum perpendicular distance from the plant path to the receiver, and the angle of θ.

83

As the major source of noise on each site was not mobile plant, the difference between this method and the method "as given" should not be very large. More measurements would need to be carried out to test this specific modification to the prediction method before any conclusions could be drawn concerning the method. However this treatment does result in mobile plant on site and plant on haul road being treated in a similar manner, giving the complete prediction method a more cohesive approach.

B.3 CONCAWE

The CONCAWE method was tested in its basic form, and with the modifications described below. Figure B6 shows graphs of predicted level plotted against measured level. The dotted reference line on each graph represents predicted level = measured level, the ideal result.

Before CONCAWE could be used at all, a method for considering mobile plant had to be devised because CONCAWE only applies to stationary plant. This was achieved by representing the moving plant as a series of point sources each operating for a proportion of the total time. This representation is adequate provided the receiver positions are not situated too close to the route of the moving plant.

B.3.1 Atmospheric Absorption

On most of the sites the measured level varied from day to day. A contributory factor to this was variation in the atmospheric absorption. However the correction for atmospheric absorption varied very little compared with the variation in the measured levels. Furthermore, the atmospheric absorption tended to be very low at those frequencies which were the dominant frequencies of the noise sources. Therefore, as a simplification to the method, the atmospheric absorption was not included.

B3.2 Meteorological Correction

The meteorological correction for the noise contribution from each source was calculated according to which meteorological category applied. There are six meteorological categories. They depend on wind speed and solar radiation during the daytime, and within one hour of sunrise or sunset or during the night they depend on cloud cover. All the comparisons for this study were made with daytime noise levels so that only the categories based on wind speed and solar radiation applied.

In addition to the above factors the component of wind speed from the source to the receiver can change the meteorological category. Therefore a small change in the wind direction can change the meteorological category which applies. A change in meteorological category can considerably affect the meteorological correction, so unless the wind speed and direction are known accurately and do not change, the resulting predicted noise level could vary by more than 10dB.

Meteorological category 4 is the "no-effect" meteorological category, or the reference category, there being no correction to be applied at any frequency for category 4. The effect of setting the meteorological category to 4 regardless of the actual conditions was investigated.

B.3.3 Barrier Attenuation and Soft Ground Attenuation

Given that surface mineral workings tend to be in rural locations it was assumed that the predominant ground type was soft.

In cases where there is considerable barrier attenuation CONCAWE includes the correction for both ground attenuation and barrier attenuation. However the presence of the barrier reduces the effect of ground attenuation so the effects are not strictly additive. The method was therefore modified to calculate both the correction for barrier attenuation and for soft ground attenuation for each source, and to use whichever one gave more attenuation to the noise level.

85

B.3.4 <u>No Meteorological Correction, and either Barrier Attenuation or Soft Ground Attenuation</u>

This combination of the two modifications described in B.3.2 and B.3.3 was investigated.

B.4 <u>Initial estimation method for opencast coal sites</u>

At the very early planning stages of a site there is insufficient detail available to use methods such as BS5228 or CONCAWE. A method has therefore been studied for use at an opencast coal site, which gives an indication of the noise levels that might be expected at positions outside the site, based on fundamental parameters such as the amount of overburden to be moved and the expected life of the site. No details of layout or topography are considered by the method.

An example calculation follows, which demonstrates the method. It was only possible to compare the predictions with measured noise levels at two positions, as the method can only be applied to positions outside the site itself. The two comparisons gave an under-prediction of 3.0 dB at Ffos Las receiver 1, and 5.3 dB at Ffos Las receiver 4. These are surprisingly good results for such a crude method, although two test positions are insufficient to judge the general accuracy.

If the accuracy of the method can be verified by tests at other opencast coal sites, it may be a useful means of providing an estimate of noise levels at the early planning stages before enough detail is known to be able to use more sophisticated methods.

B.4.1 <u>Calculation method</u>

Parameters required by the method:

    V = total volume of overburden (m^3)
    k = proportion of overburden to be moved by dump truck
    C = capacity of dump trucks (m^3)

T = round trip time for a dump truck (mins)

L = site lifetime (years)

W = number of working hours in a year

P = sound power level of a dump truck

The method assumes that the dump trucks are the dominant noise source, and calculates a sound pressure level on the basis of the rate of dump truck working:

Volume of overburden moved by dump truck = Vk

$$\text{Total number of dump truck trips} = \frac{Vk}{C}$$

$$\text{Total dump truck hours} = \frac{Vkt}{60C}$$

$$\text{Average number of dump trucks working} = \frac{Vkt}{60 \, wCL}$$

$$\text{Average sound power level} = P + 10 \log_{10} \frac{Vkt}{60 \, wCL} \text{ dB}$$

Assuming a 10dB barrier attenuation, the sound pressure level at a distance r from the centre of the site may be estimated by:

$$SPL = P + 10 \log_{10} \frac{Vkt}{60 \, wCL} - 10 \log_{10} (4 \pi r^2) - 10 \text{ dB}$$

B.4.2 Example calculation

Using data from Ffos Las opencast coal site:

Volume of overburden	$V = 49.4 \times 10^6 \text{ m}^3$
All overburden moved by dump truck	$k = 1$
Capacity of dump trucks	$C = 70 \text{m}^3$
Round trip time for dump trucks	$t = 15 \text{ mins}$
Site lifetime	$L = 11 \text{ years}$

Number of working hours in a year   W = 2750 hours
       (11hours/day, 250days/year)
Sound power level of a dump truck   P = 120 dB(A)

Approximate distances from centre of site are:
       Receiver 1 (Trimsaran) at 1000m
       Receiver 4 (Cilfery Isaf) at 1200m

Estimated SPL (receiver 1) = 120 + 7.6 - 71.0 - 10
                           = 46.6 dB(A)

Estimated SPL (receiver 4) = 120 + 7.6 - 72.6 - 10
                           = 45.0 dB(A)

ideal — 1.0   0   1.0

Modification	Correlation r	Intercept	Slope
BS5228 "as given"	0.80	8.4	0.84
CONCAWE soft ground correction or BS5228 barrier correction, whichever is the most effective	0.85	4.5	0.95
CONCAWE barrier correction	0.79	22.6	0.65
CONCAWE soft ground correction or CONCAWE barrier correction, whichever is the most effective	0.76	24.4	0.64
CRTN soft ground correction or BS5228 barrier correction, whichever is the most effective	0.73	14.1	0.79
CRTN barrier correction	0.80	11.1	0.85
CRTN soft ground correction or CRTN barrier correction, whichever is the most effective	0.67	19.7	0.71
CONCAWE soft ground correction or CRTN barrier correction, whichever is the most effective	0.79	14.8	0.80
CRTN soft ground correction or CONCAWE barrier correction, whichever is the most effective	0.73	24.0	0.65
Angle of view correction for mobile plant on site	0.76	13.9	0.77

TABLE B.1 : PREDICTION ACCURACY FOR BS5228 MODIFICATIONS

Modification	Correlation	Intercept	Slope
CONCAWE "as given"	0.79	35.3	0.46
No correction for atmospheric absorption	0.78	32.6	0.49
No correction for meterological effects	0.82	32.1	0.51
Barrier attenuation or soft ground attenuation, whichever is the most effective	0.58	40.6	0.36
Barrier attenuation or soft ground attenuation whichever is the most effective, and no correction for meteorological effects	0.82	24.9	0.60

TABLE B.2 : PREDICTION ACCURACY FOR CONCAWE MODIFICATIONS

CRTN   - CALCULATION OF ROAD TRAFFIC
               NOISE, 1988

CONCAWE - LOGARITHMIC AVERAGE OF 500,
               1k AND 2k Hz CORRECTIONS

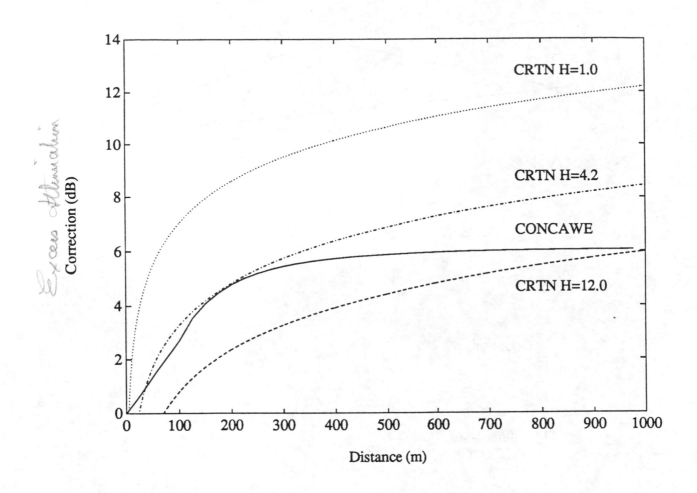

FIGURE B1 : SOFT GROUND ATTENUATION

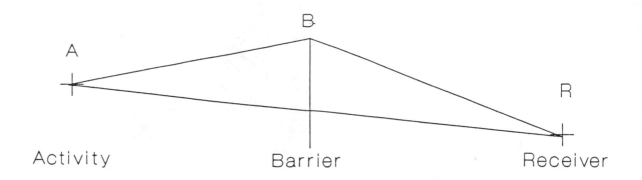

Path Difference = AB + BR - AR

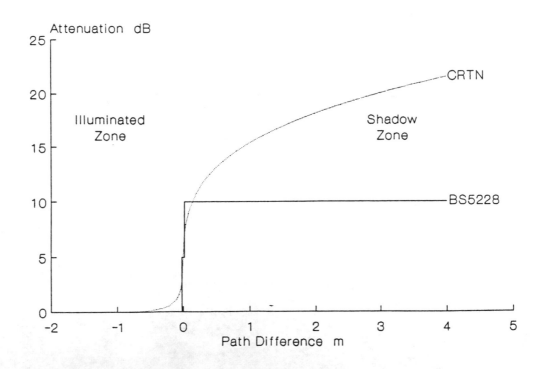

FIGURE B2 : BARRIER ATTENUATION
COMPARISON OF CRTN AND BS5228 APPROACHES

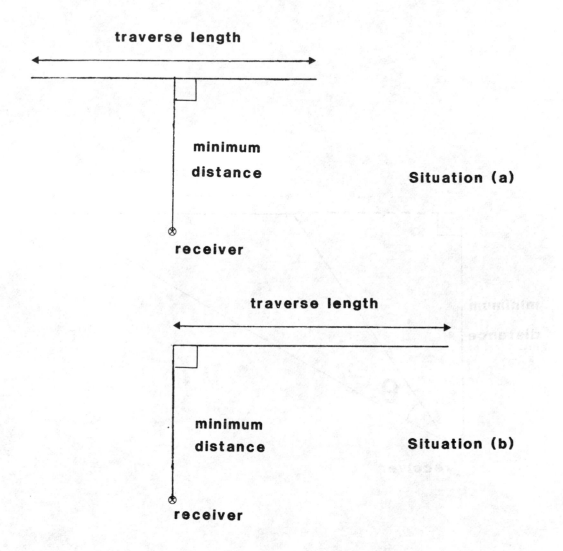

FIGURE B3 : BS5228 MOBILE PLANT ANOMALY

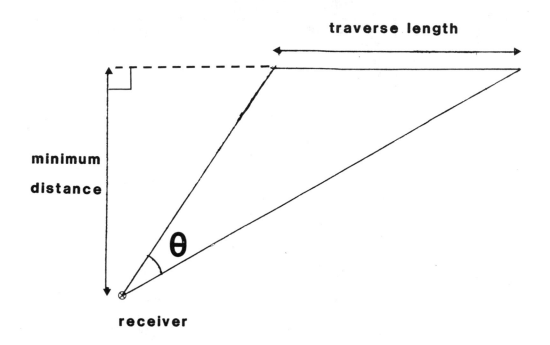

FIGURE B4 : DISTANCE CORRECTION CALCULATION

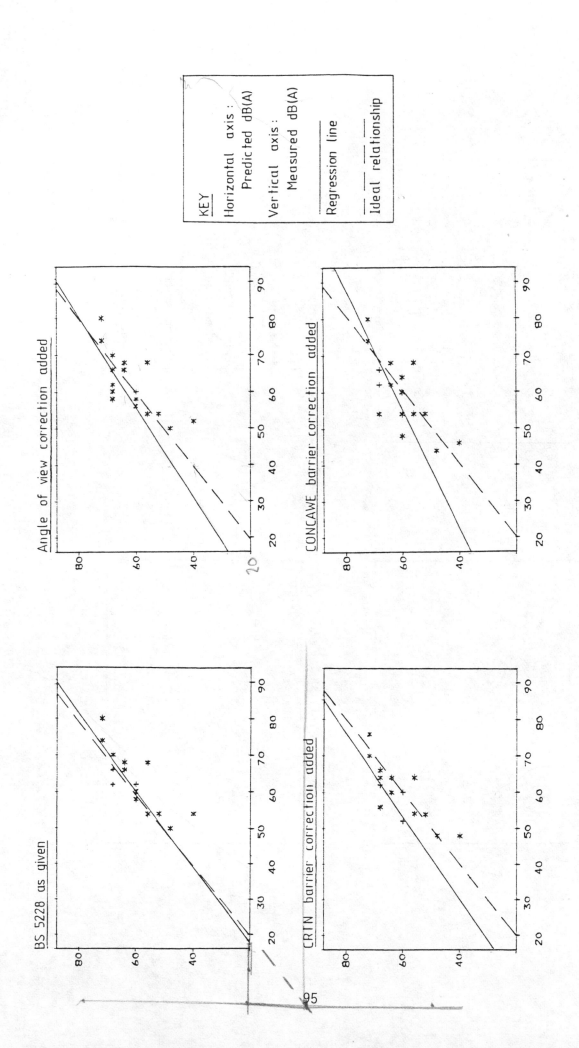

Angle of view correction added

BS 5228 as given

CONCAWE barrier correction added

CRTN barrier correction added

95

FIGURE B5(i) : BS5228 PREDICTION ACCURACIES

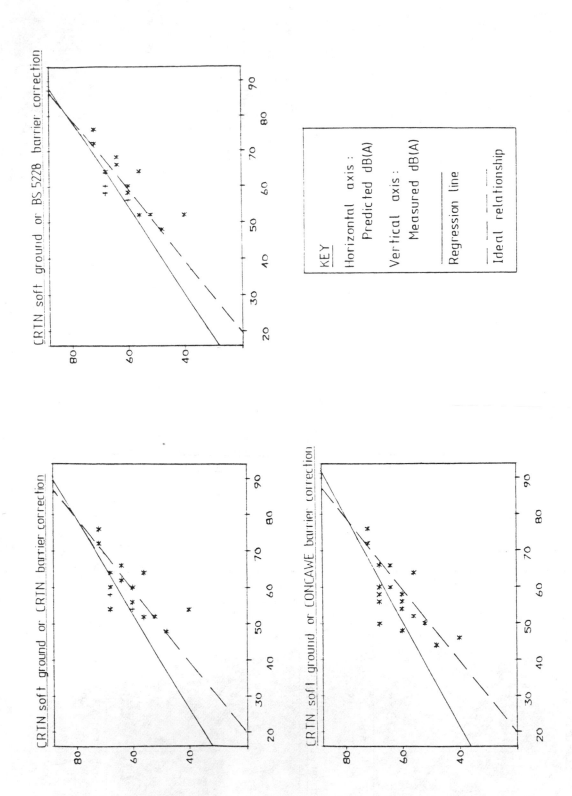

FIGURE B5(ii) : BS5228 PREDICTION ACCURACIES

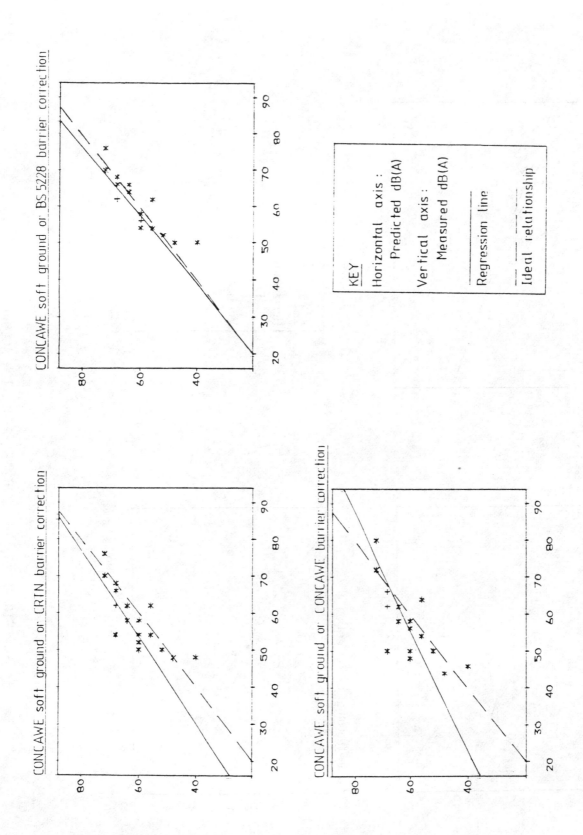

FIGURE B5(iii) : BS5228 PREDICTION ACCURACIES

97

No atmospheric correction

CONCAWE as given

No meteorological correction

KEY

Horizontal axis :
Predicted dB(A)

Vertical axis :
Measured dB(A)

——— Regression line

------- Ideal relationship

FIGURE B6(i) : CONCAWE PREDICTION ACCURACIES

98

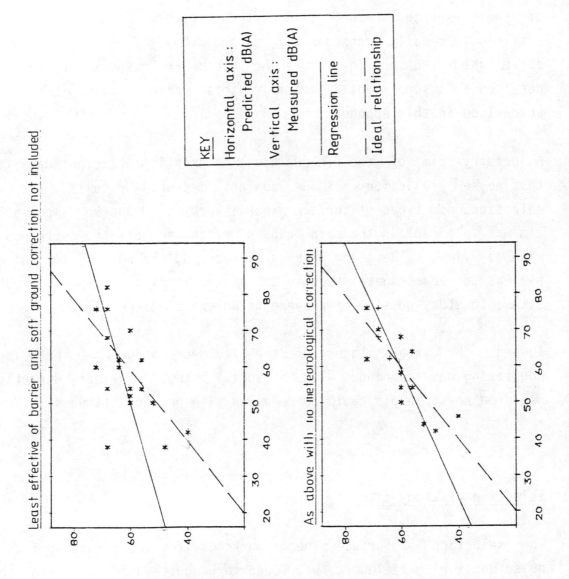

KEY

Horizontal axis :
Predicted dB(A)

Vertical axis :
Measured dB(A)

——— Regression line

— — — Ideal relationship

Least effective of barrier and soft ground correction not included

As above with no meteorological correction

FIGURE B6(ii) : CONCAVE PREDICTION ACCURACIES

99

APPENDIX C

NOISE MONITORING FIELDWORK

C.1   Purposes of fieldwork

In the early stages of the research it had been hoped that details of noise measurements made at surface mineral workings could be made available by mineral planning authorities, the site operators and environmental health departments in order to satisfy the needs of the research. However, such information was not available in sufficient detail; consequently a programme of fieldwork was established to provide it. The fieldwork results are fully detailed in a supplementary volume to this report, with the work summarised in this Appendix.

A primary aim of the fieldwork was to provide sufficient data to test noise prediction methods against measured results, for a selection of types of surface mineral workings. Another important aim was to establish the main causes of noise at the workings, with a view to devising methods of reducing the noise. The third aim was to investigate techniques of monitoring noise at such sites, to study possible improvements on existing techniques.

Towards the later stages of the fieldwork programme, the noise monitoring was combined with a social study so that directly measured noise levels could be compared with public attitudes.

C.2   Site surveys

C.2.1 Selection of study sites

The selection of surface mineral workings, for the purposes of the noise monitoring fieldwork, was found to be quite difficult due to the lack of suitable sites. It was initially decided that three sites would be surveyed, comprising an opencast coal mine, a sand and gravel pit, and a hard rock quarry. At this stage there were objections to combining the noise monitoring with the social studies, but later in the project this objection was lifted and a combined study became possible. As a result a fourth survey was also made, at another opencast coal site.

For the first three surveys, the selection criteria were that the sites should be accessible for making noise measurements at various positions within the site and close to the boundary; that there were no unusual features such as the site being under restoration; and that there were no other major noise sources to influence the measurements. In the case of the opencast coal site selection, most of the sites in the country were considered although some were soon rejected on the basis of studying their location relative to major roads. A total of 17 were visited, and most were rejected for failing to meet all the selection criteria. For the hard rock quarry, eight sites in Cumbria were considered and, as one was found suitable, no further possibilities were studied. The advice of Amey Roadstone was taken on the selection of a sand and gravel pit. The three chosen sites were East Chevington (Northumberland) opencast coal mine, Eartham (Sussex) sand and gravel pit, and Goldmire (Cumbria) limestone quarry.

For the combined noise monitoring and social survey, the main requirement was the presence of communities close to the opencast site, with the earlier criteria still applying but being less decisive. All the opencast sites were reconsidered, and five more were visited. It was surprisingly difficult to satisfy these new conditions, with only three sites having large enough communities to be feasible for the social survey although various others had small communities nearby. Of the sites considered, Ffos Las in South Wales was eventually chosen, as it had the closest communities to the workings.

It was evident from this work that there are in fact very few opencast coal mines close to large communities, and that potential noise nuisance is therefore confined to a small proportion of sites. Since only a comparatively small number of hard rock quarries and sand and gravel pits were considered, it was not possible to extend this conclusion beyond opencast sites.

101

C.2.2 Survey technique

At all four sites, measurements of the noise parameters L_{10}, L_{50}, L_{90}, L_{max} and L_{Aeq} were made over periods of typically one week, at various locations within and around the sites, with values of each parameter being recorded at between one and fifteen minute intervals. The instrumentation was developed specially as part of the research, as no commercially-available products satisfied all the requirements.

Six sets of instrumentation were constructed, allowing simultaneous measurements at up to six locations on each site. Monitoring positions were chosen to provide a range of distances away from the main workings, and to satisfy specific needs such as the measurements for comparison with the social survey.

Additionally, sound power levels were measured, with conventional hand-held equipment, of the main noise producing items of machinery on the sites. Detailed records were kept of the use and movement of machinery around the sites, of weather conditions and of working hours, all for use in the testing of prediction methods.

Contour maps of the sites were produced, where possible, from recent aerial photographs. The maps were based on a ground survey at Eartham and Goldmire as no photographs were available.

At East Chevington an additional survey, lasting three weeks, was carried out with unattended monitoring equipment to investigate patterns in noise levels over the longer term.

C.3   Application of results

C.3.1 Introduction

The data produced from the site surveys was used in the examination of prediction methods, which is reported in Section 4 and Appendix B. Its use in the identification of the main noise sources, and in the development of monitoring methods, is reported at the end of this section.

Data from the second, longer-term, East Chevington survey was used for the development of monitoring methods. This data took the form of 15-minute records over three weeks, at three measurement positions, complete with weather records. The statistical distribution of this data was examined for each position, firstly with the periods outside normal working hours removed, and secondly with the occasional breaks in working such as meal breaks and tea breaks removed as well.

C.3.2 The effect of measurement position

One of the measurement positions was about 30m from a haul road, and here the distribution of noise levels was skewed compared to a Gaussian distribution as a result of the local noise level being highly dependent on the number of dump trucks passing on that particular stretch of road. At the other two measurement positions, which were both well away from any individual noise sources, the distributions were both very close to being Gaussian. This served to demonstrate the need to measure away from individual effects to gain an overall record of the site's noise, which is standard measurement practice.

C.3.3 The effect of measurement sampling period

Taking the results from the two more distant measurement positions, standard deviations of 3.28dB and 2.9dB were calculated on the "normal working hours" data, and standard deviations of 2.50dB and 2.49dB on the "meals and tea breaks also removed" data. These values were considered to be in agreement with the subjective impression of a fairly steady noise level reaching the outer edges of the sites, not only at East Chevington but at the other three sites as well.

The improvement achieved in the standard deviation, by removing all the data relating to periods of low activity on the site, indicates the increase in reliability of measurement that can be achieved by the selection of measurement samples to coincide

103

with normal production periods. A standard deviation of 2.5dB would appear to be achievable at opencast sites, although further long-term measurements at a variety of types of surface mineral working would be needed to verify whether this would apply to all types of working. It would seem likely that similar standard deviations might apply, based on a subjective impression that the degree of variation in noise levels at the different types of mineral working are similar.

The implications of a 2.5dB standard deviation on measurement accuracy are demonstrated in figure C1. This indicates the highest true mean 15-minute L_{Aeq} that might be expected, given a measured mean based on a certain number of measurements, expressed as a value to be added to the measured mean. Four curves are shown, for different confidence levels. Commonly a 95% confidence level is considered adequate to correspond with 'engineering accuracy' and so this curve has been discussed further in section 4.2. All four curves are produced by assuming a normal distribution of the noise levels, and applying standard statistical techniques.

C.3.4 Main sources of noise

In order to establish from the monitoring data the main sources of noise on the mineral workings, the measured sound power levels of individual items of equipment may be studied. These are summarised in Table C.1.

It is evident that on opencast coal sites the dump trucks have the highest sound power levels. Their influence on overall noise levels is increased further by their weight of numbers, with 10 or 20 trucks being common. Ancillary diesel-driven equipment such as water bowsers and scrapers have sound power levels close to those of dump trucks and are therefore important, although there will normally only be one or two of each of these on a site. Bulldozers have similar sound power levels when under load, for example when shovelling overburden, but are only in use occasionally so are less important. Of the stationary equipment, electrically operated items (including draglines and rope excavators) are very quiet in comparison with the machinery mentioned above, although diesel powered equipment such as the Demag backactor at Ffos Las can be an important noise source.

The main noise sources at hard rock quarries and sand and gravel workings are seen to be different to those at opencast coal sites. Noise from fixed process machinery, which tends to operate continuously, is the most significant. The machinery normally comprising a series of crushers and graders. The rate of movement of material on these sites tends to be somewhat lower than at opencast coal sites so that material may be carried by conveyor belt or by just one or two dump trucks making infrequent trips, so that this type of noise becomes correspondingly less significant.

Item	Sound power level dB(A)	Item	Sound power level dB(A)
East Chevington		Ffos Las	
Dump truck (unladen, flat)	112.6	Terex dump truck (laden, uphill)	114.8
Dump truck (laden, flat)	120.8	Terex dump truck (unladen, down)	113.2
Dump truck (unladen, down)	116.8	Cat dump truck (laden, uphill)	117.2
Dump truck (laden, uphill)	119.3	Cat dump truck (unladen, down)	113.3
Air compressor	99.6	Water bowser	115.9
Scraper	112.6	Demag backactor	114.9
Coal lorry (unladen)	108.5	Coal lorry (laden, up)	111.0
Coal lorry (laden)	106.9	Coal lorry (unladen, down)	100.9
Bulldozer (shovelling)	117.1		
Water pump	105.1		
Water bowser	117.7		
Goldmire		Eartham	
Crushers & graders	112.5	Crushers & Graders	110.6
Shovel	107.7	Shovel	112.4
Blasthole drilling	119.9	Dragline (diesel)	103.2
Tarmacadam coating	109.2		

TABLE C1   SUMMARY OF SOUND POWER LEVELS

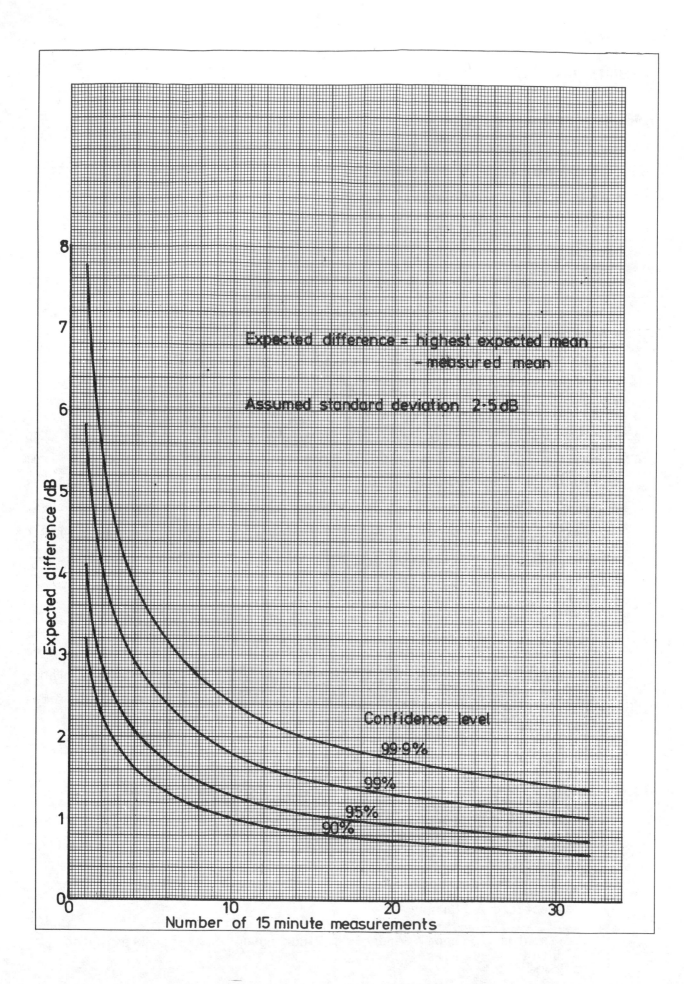

FIGURE C.1 NOISE MEASUREMENT ACCURACY

APPENDIX D

COMMUNITY RESPONSE TO NOISE

D.1 The study was conducted in two phases, the first designed to be exploratory and the second to provide a quantitative assessment of the impact of noise from surface mineral workings.

D.2 Phase One Survey

The survey results include three types of information. Responses were gained from a questionnaire administered to residents in their homes which addressed a range of issues concerning the local community and environment. This pre-panel survey was used primarily to screen, select and recruit participants for panel discussion meetings. A series of local panel meetings were then held. Outputs from the meetings include an individual questionnaire and results from structured, but open discussions chaired by W.S Atkins professional staff. Finally, district environmental health and planning officers, and site engineers of SMW sites, were interviewed to gain their experience and perception of community response issues.

D.2.1 Survey Locations

124 individuals were interviewed in the two districts surveyed. From this total, 54 were selected to attend the six panel meetings; three meetings were held in each community. The communities and SMW sites studied are listed in Table D.1.

Table D.1 Community Response Survey Sites - Phase One

Cumbria (Allerdale)		Northumberland (Castle Morpeth)	
Community	SMW	Community	SMW
Broughton	Low Close (Opencast)	Red Row	East Chevington
Brigham/ Eaglesfield	Tendley Quarry	Hadston	East Chevington
Westnewton/ Aldoth/ Aikshaw	Local Sand Pits	Widdrington	West Chevington

In each of the communities surveyed, local residents welcomed interest in their views about their own community and environment.

D2.2   Findings

The findings indicate that - leaving aside the possibly severe noise impacts on residents of adjacent properties, and at certain stages of a site's operations - noise is a problem of some, but not major community importance. When it does figure as a nuisance, noise is mostly related to the whole set of environmental effects created by SMW traffic moving to and from sites. It was also found that some effects, particularly dust, rate higher as a cause of concern than noise.

D2.3   Pre-Panel Survey Results

The pre-panel individual interviews in the two districts show some interesting differences. There was an immediate adverse reaction to opencast mining in Castle Morpeth which residents linked with dust levels. In Allerdale, the link between negative rated features of the environment and SMW appeared at most indirect. The results could be consistent with the identification of SMW noise as a community problem. At this stage of the investigation, however, the responses were of a very general kind and relate more to rural peace than SMW activity.

Respondents were asked for their likes and dislikes concerning the local area. Unprompted questions of this kind give a good idea of the everyday importance given to the factors they mention.

Many residents in both districts felt very positive about the quietness of their surroundings and the general scenery and countryside aspects of the area. Positive descriptions were also given of village life and its associated privacy.

At the same time, a number of residents of Castle Morpeth stated their dislike, unprompted, of adjacent opencast coal sites. A far less marked response towards SMW was found for the Allerdale sample. Table D.2 shows that Allerdale residents were more satisfied with their community and environment than Castle Morpeth residents.

Residents were then asked to rate selected characteristics of the physical and socioeconomic environment. In both districts there was a relatively high degree of consensus on the importance of jobs and housing. Most residents were dissatisfied with the current levels of employment and satisfied with the availability of local housing. There was far less agreement in rating other variables which were potentially SMW related. Questions were asked about the "protection of the environment" and "industrial nuisance". For those respondents interviewed who were inclined to evidence a consistently hostile attitude to SMW, these two questions gave them the opportunity to record their dissatisfaction. In fact, the number of those dissatisfied and satisfied were of roughly equal proportions, though in Allerdale, slightly more were concerned with environmental protection than not.

Questions then focused more directly on the specific attributes of the local physical environment. Residents in both districts agreed strongly that their's was a peaceful spot, confirming their earlier unprompted descriptions. At the same time, over 50% of the responses in both districts perceived their local environment as noisy during certain times of the day. This could indicate sensitivity to noise, and that the offending noise is intermittent. This response, may, therefore, be related to SMW activity.

The only attribute of the physical environment in which both districts greatly differed was that relating to dust. The Castle Morpeth area is perceived as a much dustier place than Allerdale. This is directly attributed, by some residents, to the opencast sites.

The final section of this questionnaire gave a list of potential priorities for community and local environment improvement. Respondents were asked to choose those priorities they felt most relevant to their area. In Allerdale, more jobs, an improved public transport service and better environmental protection were the three highest priorities. In Castle Morpeth, jobs were again first, followed by improved shopping facilities, and a better police service. The overall pattern of response to this question is similar to that found for the question which asked for unprompted descriptions of each area.

D2.4 Responses of Individual Panel Members

The results of the questionnaire completed by individual panel members before the start of the collective discussion show that, although noise was an environmental issue, it was not particularly bothersome. Attention focused on other environmental factors, some of which might relate to SMW operations.

Respondents are aware of noise from sources more distant than the adjacent houses. Few residents, however, were especially bothered by the level of noise concerned. Panellists in each district were, however, concerned about the damage that may be caused by vibration. We should note at the same time, that they also recorded strongly that their area needed more industry.

Panellists were asked to nominate, from a list their three priorities for improving the local environment. Allerdale respondents gave improved traffic planning, and controls on housing/building as their highest priorities.

Priorites in Castle Morpeth were different. Residents were in strong agreement that the highest priority was the control of dust. Improving the landscape and the reduction of noise were also relatively high priorites.

D2.5 Results of Panel Discussions

When panellists were asked, as a group, to rank possible improvements to the local environment, noise did emerge as issue. But this is almost always related to off-site traffic, and as part of a complex of adversely rated environmental effects. It cannot be said, however, that the panels were unusually bothered by the impact of SMW, except for one or possibly two out of the six. In both districts, one of the panels wished to focus a great deal of attention on SMW activities, and of these two, one - adjacent to a limestone quarry in Allerdale - was particularly marked with negative reaction to SMW. The other four groups were much more concerned with the social and economic features of their village, and less so with the details of its physical environment.

Towards the conclusion of each panel meeting panellists were again asked to choose their priorities for improving the local environment, but this time as a group. The two districts had very different responses. The three panel groups in Allerdale were unanimous in agreeing that the highest priority was for improved traffic planning and controls. Two of the groups linked this specifically with traffic travelling to and from SMW. These two groups also felt that a reduction in noise, vibration, and dust would all follow closely if further traffic planning controls were implemented.

Two of the three panel groups in Castle Morpeth placed jobs as their highest priority. They echoed earlier concerns for better shopping facilities and an improved police service. Only the control of dust was explicitly linked to SMW.

The other Castle Morpeth panel group (Widdrington) had a very different set of priorities. Their major concerns were almost all connected with the nearby opencast site. Their highest priority was to improve the appearance of the landscape. They wanted improvements to baffle mounds in order to hide SMW operations and to lessen dust and noise impacts. The high priority they gave to improve traffic planning was connected to nuisance from the amount of traffic travelling to and from the sites.

D2.6 Site Engineers, Environmental Health & Planning Officers

The above findings are in agreement with the views obtained from site engineers, environmental health and planning officers. The number and level of complaints about noise are not great and usually limited to specific phases of a site's operation. Most complaints are about other factors. On the whole, the site engineers are vigilant in their attention to potential noise hazards. The environmental health officers interviewed agreed that appropriate planning and site controls can cope with noise hazards. They acknowledged that there was a need for widely accepted and consistent control standards.

D.3 Phase Two Study

D.3.1 The Phase two study was intended to concentrate on noise, and to assess quantitatively its impact on local residents. At an early stage it was decided to concentrate on a single site thereby holding many non-noise variables constant, rather than to attempt to collect a large database to statistically control non-noise variables.

In spite of an extended search, described in Appendix C2 above, it was not possible to find an ideal site for such a survey, and the selection of Ffos Las was that of a least worse option. While there are two communities, Trimsaran and Carway, close to the site, the detailed survey showed that neither is exposed to on-site noise which is measurably above the background noise level. It is therefore not possible to provide an analysis in the conventional dose-response form, in which measured noise levels are correlated with subjective evaluations of noise annoyance.

While this limits the scope of the research, it is some indication of the success of the site management team in controlling the impact of noise on local residents. The fact that site activities were clearly audible from several points to the east of the site, where housing is very sparse and the dominating land-use is agricultural, further supports this point.

Ffos Las is a large opencast site operated by Wimpey Mining for the Opencast Executive. Trimsaran is the larger of the two villages and is to the SW of the site. It is built on a rising slope but this faces roughly ENE, and hence does not increase the noise exposure to on-site activities. Carway is to the NE of the site and is of a simpler form than Trimsaran, basically linear and parallel to the site boundary.

A total of 222 residents were interviewed. Their responses will here be considered as providing answers to a set of underlying questions.

Table D.2 - Unprompted Descriptions of the Local Area

Positive Features

	Cumbria (Allerdale)	Northumberland (Castle Morpeth)
Scenery/countryside	40	19
Quiet	30	26
The people (friendly)	14	9
Village life	10	4
Beach/coast	-	13
Privacy	5	5
Unpolluted/ unlittered	8	
Access (work/shops/ towns)	5	4
Environment	5	1
Born here	1	4
Everything	2	1
Safe	2	-
Nothing	-	2
Good amenities	1	-
Local sports	1	-
No vandalism	1	-
Local pub	1	-
Local schools	1	-
Good land	-	1

	Cumbria (Allerdale)	Northumberland (Castle Morpeth)
Total Respondents	62	62
Total Responses	129	89

Negative Features

	Cumbria (Allerdale)	Northumberland (Castle Morpeth)
Lack of amenities	14	15
There are none	17	8
Public transport	15	10
Surface mineral workings	4	20
Traffic/roads (inc. lorries)	14	4
Lack of entertainment	7	9
Loss of old village life	-	5
No jobs	-	4
The people here	-	3
Access (distances)	3	-
Vandalism	-	3
Isolated/quiet	-	3
Weather	2	1
Proposed nuclear power station	-	3
By-pass	-	2
Sellafield	2	-
Low-flying aircraft	-	2
Old buildings	-	2
Noise	-	1
Unhelpful local attitudes	1	-
Lack of communication	1	-
Poor Council	1	-
The local environment	1	-
Power cuts	1	-
Nearby industry	1	-
Diesel pollution	1	-
Local prison	-	1
Big community centre	-	1
Neglect of trees	-	1
Restricted access for walking	-	1
No telephones	-	1
Too flat	-	1
Dead animals	-	1
No local gas	-	1
People cutting through gardens	-	1

	Cumbria (Allerdale)	Northumberland (Castle Morpeth)
Total Respondents	62	62
Total Responses	85	104

D3.2 **Do respondents discriminate between the various environmental aspects, or do they respond globally to the overall impact of the opencast works?**

Respondents were asked to rate their annoyance with noise, with dust, and with the visual appearance of the works. If respondents responded globally, showing the so-called 'halo effect' there would be a strong and significant association between these three judgements. It would be possible to predict, with a high degree of confidence, from a knowledge of one rating what the other two ratings would be. Table D.3 shows that though there was a significant association between all pairs of variables as shown by the Kendall's Tau C values, the association was far from strong, as shown by the lambda values. The lambda statistic is of the proportional reduction in uncertainty type, and is an indication of how much knowledge of one rating helps in predicting another rating. Thus, knowing the rating of dust removes only 22.2% of the uncertainty about the rating of noise.

From this, it is clear that respondents do discriminate between these three aspects.

Table D.3

Statistical Relationship between Environmental Aspects

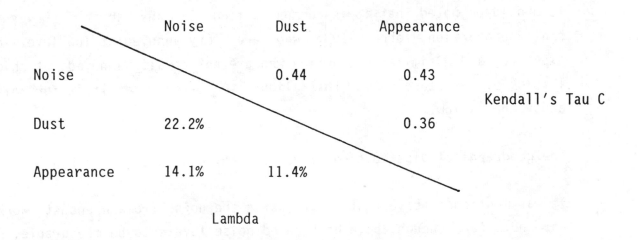

	Noise	Dust	Appearance	
Noise		0.44	0.43	
				Kendall's Tau C
Dust	22.2%		0.36	
Appearance	14.1%	11.4%		

Lambda

D.3.3 **Which aspects of the opencast works are most noticed in daily life, and which cause most annoyance?**

When respondents were asked which single aspect of the opencast works they most noticed in the course of their daily life, noise was clearly the most frequent response (35%) dust second (26%) and appearance third (14%). Traffic which had emerged as a major problem in Phase One was the most noticed aspect for only 7% of respondents at Ffos Las. This difference may be in part due to good traffic planning which keeps coal lorries travelling between the site and the washing station well away from homes.

When the question is changed, to which aspect is most annoying, a different pattern emerges. Respondents rated each aspect on a scale of : extremely annoying, very annoying, moderately annoying, slightly annoying, not at all annoying. Grouping the two higher and two lower levels of annoyance together produces the following result:

	2 Higher Levels	2 Lower Levels
Noise	15.7%	71%
Appearance	18.6%	64.5%
Dust	33%	50%

It should be noted that it is common to find, in any social survey a small proportion, about 10%, who are very annoyed at low levels of exposure, and a similar proportion who are not at all annoyed at high levels of exposure. In that light the figure of 15.7% for noise annoyance is low.

The geographical distribution of noise annoyance is shown in Fig D.1.

It was mentioned above that in Trimsaran the noise from opencast works was not far enough above background noise levels to be measurable, so that it is not possible to relate noise annoyance to measured noise exposure.

However it is possible to predict noise exposures which are below background level, using the best predictor as selected in Appendix B. Such an exercise was performed for a grid of 13 points in Trimsaran.

The results show that, not only is the exposure level low, but the variation in exposure level is restricted. The highest and lowest values were 47.7 and 43.3 dB(A) respectively.

It is clear that the potential problem of noise is to a large extent contained, but the problem of dust is more acute.

D.3.4 What sources of noise cause most annoyance?

For 40% of those who are moderately, very or extremely annoyed by noise from the open cast workings the dominant cause of annoyance is reversing alarms. This dominance seems to increase with the level of annoyance. Thus 50% of those who are extremely annoyed cite reversing alarms as the cause, as against 44% of those who are very annoyed, and 33% of those who are moderately annoyed.

Given the above it would seem worthwhile investigating reversing alarms to reduce their intrusiveness off-site. However the problem is not easily solved. It is in conflict with providing a safe attention-demanding warning signal on site.

And as shown in Figure D.2 reversing alarms are a source of annoyance throughout the study area, even though at considerable distances and with intervening barriers, the physical sound pressure level is well below the background noise level.

This point is further supported by responses to another question concerned with the qualities of sounds which were found to be annoying. Of those who were moderately, very or extremely annoyed only 5% cited loudness, whereas for 35% it was the Tonal quality, and for a further 40% the repetitiveness of the noise that was felt to be annoying.

D.3.5 Does noise annoyance get less over time?

31% of respondents felt that the amount of noise they now experienced differed from that when the workings started. Approximately two thirds of these felt they were less annoyed as against one third who were more annoyed. This evidence would seem to indicate a degree of adaptation.

But there is no evidence that those who have lived longer at their present residence are any more or less likely to be annoyed by noise than others. However since the vast majority (77%) have lived at their present address for more than 5 years, evidence of adaptation is unlikely to be revealed in this way.

D.3.6 Are certain types of people more annoyed by noise than others?

There is no indication from this survey that noise annoyance is related to gender, to the amount of time that is spent at home, to occupation, or to whether one's job is connected with mining.

There is a more frequent incidence of the higher levels of noise annoyance amongst those whose family mostly use a room facing towards the open cast works. Thus 18.9% of those who mostly use a room facing towards the open cast works report that they are extremely or very annoyed by noise, whereas for those mostly using a room that does not face the works only 11% rate themselves as extremely or very annoyed. Correspondingly, lower levels of annoyance are more frequent when the most-used room faces away from the workings (77%) than when it faces towards the workings (59%). However these differences just fail to reach the 5% significance level (chi square = 3.31; for p= 0.05 chi square = 3.84).

D.3.7 Do the responses of the two communities differ?

Apart from 3 respondents the remainder lived in Trimsaran (166) or in Carway (58). There are some interesting differences in the responses from the two villages.

When asked which aspect of the open cast workings they most noticed in the course of their daily life 40% of the respondents from Carway mentioned dust, and 34% mentioned noise. The percentages for Trimsaran were different, 22% and 35% respectively. As can be seen the difference arises from the greater proportion of Carway residents citing dust. (Carway is in the lee of Ffos Las, and Trimsaran to the windward side).

Carway residents were twice as likely to rate their noise annoyance level as extremely or very annoying as residents of Trimsaran (25% and 12% respectively). This need not be surprising as Carway is a linear settlement stretched along the boundary of the workings, whereas Trimsaran is much more complex in form, and many residents were distant from the site boundary.

Carway residents were also three times as likely to be extremely or very annoyed by dust as were Trimsaran residents (66% as against 22%, see Fig D.3) and more than twice as likely to be extremely or very annoyed by the appearance of the works (29% as against 12%).

Whether these differences in response are because of a difference in exposure levels, or because the residents of Carway are, for some unknown reason, more difficult to satisfy than those of Trimsaran, can not be finally answered by this survey.

FIGURE D.1

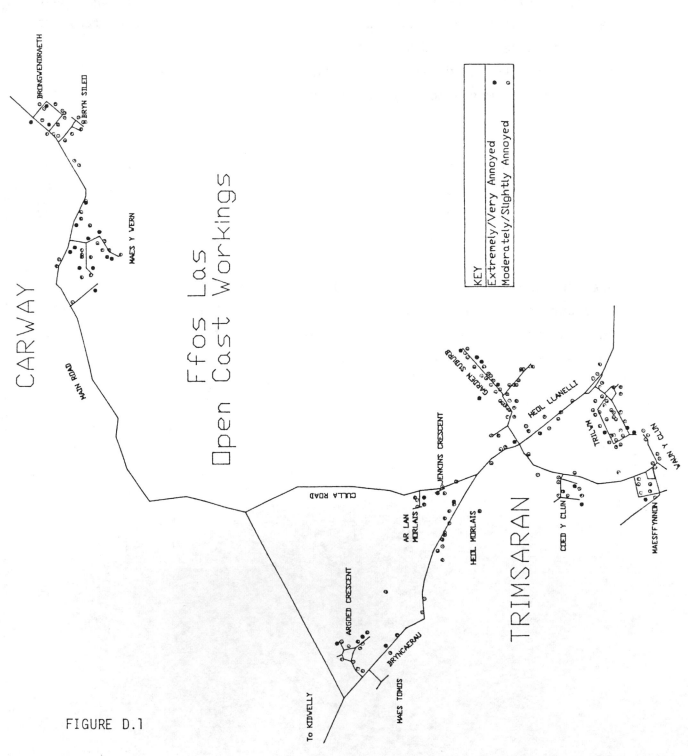

Distribution of respondents annoyance at noise from open cast.

FIGURE D.2

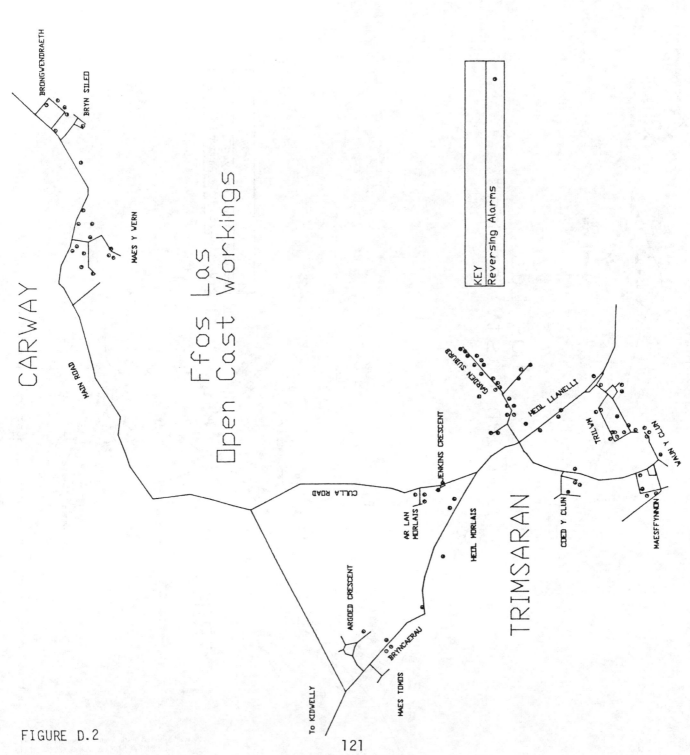

KEY

Reversing Alarms

Distribution of respondents who state that reversing alarms are the main cause of noise from open cast.

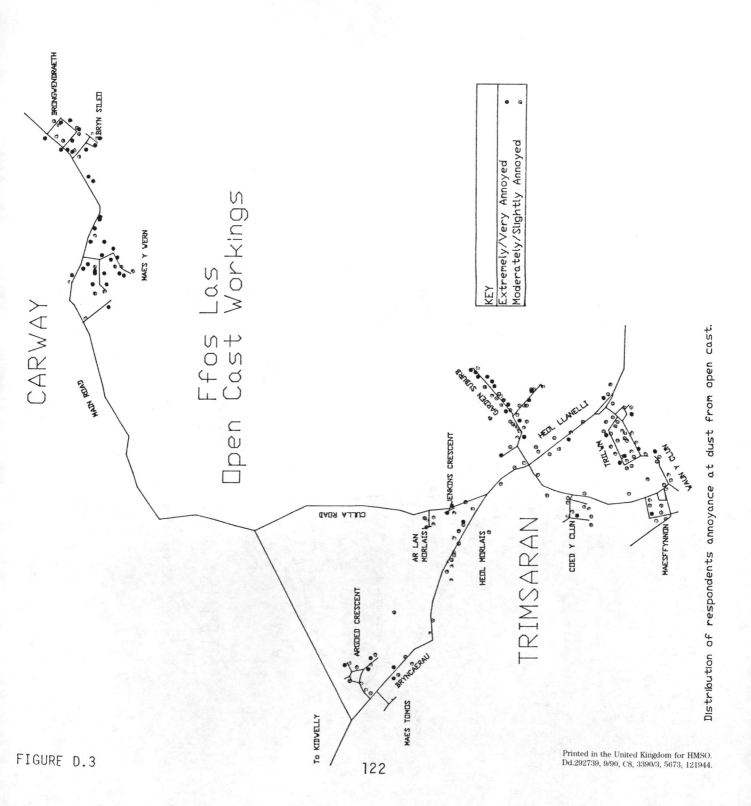

FIGURE D.3

CARWAY

Ffos Las
Open Cast Workings

BRONGWENDRAETH

BRYN SILED

MAES Y VERN

MAIN ROAD

CULLA ROAD

To KIDWELLY

ARGOED CRESCENT

BRYNCAERAU

MAES TOMOS

AR LAN MORLAIS

JENKINS CRESCENT

HEOL MORLAIS

GARDEN SUBURB

HEOL LLANELLI

COED Y CLUN

TRILYN

VANY CLUN

MAESFFYNNON

TRIMSARAN

KEY

Extremely/Very Annoyed

Moderately/Slightly Annoyed

Distribution of respondents annoyance at dust from open cast.

122

Printed in the United Kingdom for HMSO.
Dd.292739, 9/90, C8, 3390/3, 5673, 121944.